AQA Biology

Revision Guide

A LEVEL YEAR 2

David Applin

OXFORD

UNIVERSITY PRESS

OXFORD
UNIVERSITY PRESS

Great Clarendon Street, Oxford, OX2 6DP, United Kingdom

Oxford University Press is a department of the University of Oxford. It furthers the University's objective of excellence in research, scholarship, and education by publishing worldwide. Oxford is a registered trade mark of Oxford University Press in the UK and in certain other countries

First published in 2017

British Library Cataloguing in Publication Data
Data available

978 0 19 835773 5

10 9 8 7 6 5 4 3 2 1

Printed in Great Britain by CPI Anthony Rowe

Acknowledgements

Cover: Blend Images Photography/Veer

Artwork by Q2A Media

AS/A Level course structure

This book has been written to support students studying for A Level Biology. It covers the Year 2 sections from the specification, the content of which will also be examined at A Level. The sections covered are shown in the contents list, which also shows you the page numbers for the main topics within each section.

AS exam

Year 1 content

1 Biological molecules
2 Cells
3 Organisms exchange substances with their environment
4 Genetic information, variation, and relationships between organisms

Year 2 content

5 Energy transfers in and between organisms
6 Organisms respond to changes in their internal and external environment
7 Genetics, populations, evolution, and ecosystems
8 The control of gene expression

A level exam

A Level exams will cover content from Year 1 and Year 2 and will be at a higher demand.

Contents

How to use this book

This book contains many different features. Each feature is designed to support and develop the skills you will need for your examinations, as well as foster and stimulate your interest in biology.

 Go further

To push you a little further.

Common misconception

Common student misunderstandings clarified.

Question and model answers

Sample answers to exam style-style questions.

Summary questions

1 These are short questions at the end of each topic.

2 They test your understanding of the topic and allow you to apply the knowledge and skills you have acquired.

3 The questions are ramped in order of difficulty. Lower-demand questions have a paler background, with the higher-demand questions having a darker background. Try to attempt every question you can, to help you achieve your best in the exams.

Specification references

→ At the beginning of each topic, there are specification references to allow you to monitor your progress.

Key term

Pulls out key terms for quick reference.

Synoptic link

These highlight how the sections relate to each other. Linking different areas of biology together becomes increasingly important, as many exam questions (particularly at A Level) will require you to bring together your knowledge from different areas.

Revision tip

Prompts to help you with your revision.

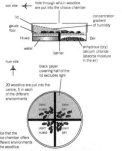

Chapter 14 Practice questions

Practice questions at the end of each chapter including questions that cover practical and maths skills.

Synoptic link

For more information on photosynthesis, see Topic 11.2, The light-dependent reaction, Topic 11.3, The light-independent reaction, Topic 2.3, Energy and ATP, and Topic 3.4, Eukaryotic cell structure.

Photosynthesis: preview

Plants fix carbon dioxide and water, forming triose sugar. Light is the source of energy which drives the reactions. The reactions are the components of photosynthesis. It is a reduction process in which carbon dioxide is reduced by hydrogen derived from water. The reactions occur in **chloroplasts**.

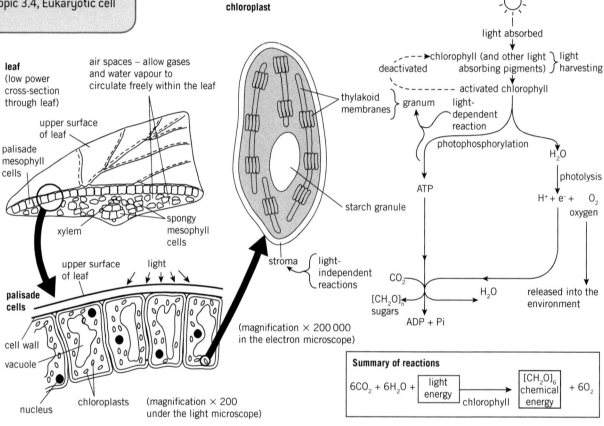

▲ **Figure 1** *Leaf cells and chloroplasts. Chlorophyll and other light-absorbing pigments cover the thylakoid membranes of each granum. Their large surface area maximises the capture of light. The light-dependent reaction occurs on the thylakoid membranes; the light-independent reaction occurs in the stroma*

Light harvesting – light energy is captured by chlorophyll and other light-absorbing pigments.

Light-dependent reaction – captured light energy splits water into hydrogen ions (H⁺) and oxygen. The process is called **photolysis**. The light energy is converted into the bond energy of ATP, and NADP is reduced by hydrogen ions. The process is called **photophosphorylation**.

Light-independent reaction – hydrogen ions (H⁺) released by photolysis combine with carbon dioxide, reducing it. Triose sugar is formed. **Leaf adaptations** maximise the rate of photosynthesis.

The palisade mesophyll cells just under the transparent cuticle and cells of the upper epidermis are elongated. Elongation funnels light to the spongy mesophyll cells beneath. Palisade cells and spongy cells are packed with chloroplasts. Leaves are thin, and cover a large surface area, maximising the absorption of light. Leaves tend not to overlap. This leaf mosaic avoids leaves overshadowing one another. Numerous stomata perforate the lower leaf surface, enabling gases and water vapour to diffuse freely into and out of the leaf.

Summary questions

1 Summarise the different stages of photosynthesis. *(4 marks)*
2 Adaptations of the leaf maximise the rate of photosynthesis. Explain how. *(4 marks)*

3 Explain how the structure of a chloroplast maximises the rate of photosynthesis. *(4 marks)*

11.2 The light-dependent reaction

Specification reference: 3.5.1

Pigments and thylakoid membranes

A pigment is a substance that absorbs light. **Chlorophylls**, **carotenes**, and **xanthophylls** are photosynthetic pigments. They each absorb slightly different wavelengths of the spectrum of visible light, except green which is mostly reflected.

As a result, most of the spectrum of visible light is absorbed by the pigments, maximising the amount of energy available for photosynthesis.

Different types of photosystem work together at the same time. In Figure 2, they are labelled PSI and PSII. They pass electrons to acceptor molecules, labelled 1 and 2, which in turn transfer the electrons to the proteins of different electron transfer chains. Energy is released and used to make ATP from the combination of an ADP molecule with an inorganic phosphate group. Electrons are also transferred to an electron carrier called **nicotinamide adenine dinucleotide phosphate** (NADP), reducing it. The electron transfers result in the **light-dependent reaction**; see Figure 2 and Stages 1–5 below for details.

Stage 1

Light energy is absorbed by PSII. The electrons of a pigment molecule are raised to a higher energy level, released, and captured by electron acceptor 1. Now oxidised, the loss of electrons from the pigment molecule is repaid by electrons gained from the photolysis of water. Remember that photolysis also produces protons (H^+) and that oxygen gas is released.

Stage 2

Electrons transfer from electron acceptor 1 along an electron transfer chain to PSI. The transfer of electrons is by a series of redox reactions similar to that of the electron transport chain of the inner mitochondrial membrane. Energy is released, enabling ADP and inorganic phosphate (P_i) to combine, forming ATP. Light energy has therefore been converted to and stored as chemical bond energy in molecules of ATP. The process is called non-cyclic photophosphorylation, as its reactions follow a linear metabolic pathway.

Stage 3

Light energy is absorbed by PSI. The electrons of a pigment molecule are raised to a higher energy level. The electrons are released and captured by electron acceptor 2. Now oxidised, the loss of electrons from the pigment molecules is repaid by electrons gained from the chain of electron carriers described in Stage 2.

light energy absorbed passes
between pigment molecules

accessory
pigment
molecules

photosystem

reaction centre
chlorophyll molecule
(primary pigment)

electron released from pigment molecule
and passes to electron acceptor

e⁻

thylakoid
membrane

electron acceptor
molecule

thylakoid space

stroma

▲ **Figure 1** *Photosystems absorb light energy*

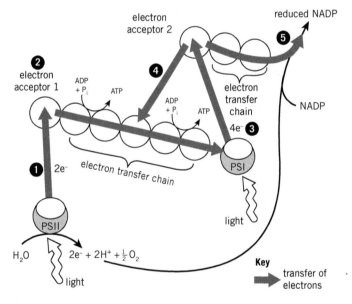

▲ **Figure 2** *The light-dependent reaction of photosynthesis*

3

Synoptic link

See Topic 11.1, Overview of photosynthesis, Topic 11.3, The light-independent reaction, Topic 2.3, Energy and ATP, and Topic 12.3, Oxidative phosphorylation.

Reviewing Topic 2.3, Energy and ATP will help you link the topic with the light-dependent reaction.

Go further

Like the electron chain of the inner mitochondrial membrane, the electron transport chain linking the primary electron acceptor 1 to photosystem 1 consists of different proteins that transfer electrons along the chain in a series of redox reactions.

a What are redox reactions?

b What is the result of electron transfer along the electron transfer chain in chloroplasts?

Stage 4

Some electrons from electron acceptor 2 pass back to PSI by the chain of electron carriers described in Stage 2. Another molecule of ATP is generated. Because electrons are recycled, the process is called cyclic photophosphorylation.

Stage 5

Electrons transfer from electron acceptor 2 along a chain of electron carriers to nicotinamide adenine dinucleotide phosphate (NADP). They combine with the protons (H^+) released by photolysis (see Stage 1) and NADP is reduced.

Absorbing light

The photosynthetic pigments are part of the thylakoid membranes. The molecules of pigment absorb light energy.

Absorption of light energy by a pigment molecule boosts the energy of a pair of its electrons. As a result:

- the energy levels of the electrons are raised
- the electrons are released
- the chlorophyll molecule is oxidised and positively charged.

Photosynthetic pigments are organised into units called photosystems. Note that electrons released from a photosystem pass to an electron acceptor.

Summary questions

1 Why is chlorophyll called a pigment?   (1 mark)

2 What are the sources of electrons transferred to electron acceptor 1 and electron acceptor 2?   (2 marks)

11.3 The light-independent reaction

Specification reference: 3.5.1

The Calvin cycle

The light-independent reaction of photosynthesis takes place in the stroma of chloroplasts. It occurs whether or not light is available. The sequence of reactions is sometimes called the **Calvin cycle**. Like the Krebs cycle, the end product of the reactions regenerates the starting substance of the process. Figure 1 and Stages 1 to 4 are your guide to the details of the light-independent reaction.

Stage 1

Carbon dioxide in solution (dissociated as H^+ and HCO_3^- ions) diffuses through the plasma membrane, through the cytoplasm, and through the membrane surrounding the chloroplasts of photosynthetic cells. In the stroma, it combines with the 5-carbon compound ribulose bisphosphate (RuBP), producing an unstable 6-carbon molecule that immediately splits into two 3-carbon molecules of glycerate 3-phosphate (GP). The reaction is catalysed by the enzyme rubisco, located on the surface of the thylakoid membranes.

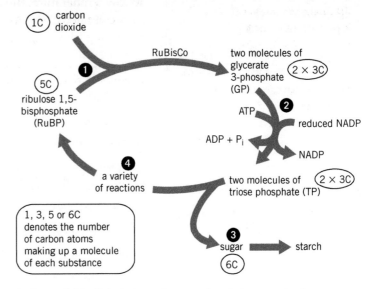

▲ **Figure 1** *The light-independent reaction of photosynthesis*

Stage 2

GP is reduced to triose phosphate (TP), by reduced NADP produced in the light-dependent reactions. TP is a phosphorylated triose sugar. The reaction is endothermic and driven by the ATP produced during photophosphorylation. NADP is regenerated and is available to accept more protons (H^+) released by photolysis during the light-dependent reactions.

Stage 3

The combination of two molecules of TP produces a molecule of glucose (hexose sugar). The combination of many glucose molecules forms starch.

Stage 4

Other molecules of TP combine in a variety of reactions, regenerating RuBP. Overall five molecules of GALP combine to form three molecules of RuBP. The process uses ATP produced by photophosphorylation during the light-dependent reaction.

Why are limiting factors limiting?

The rate of photosynthesis determines the mass of triose sugar produced in a given time. It is affected by supplies of carbon dioxide and water, temperature, and the intensity of light. These factors are called *limiting factors* because if any one of them falls to a low level the rate of photosynthesis slows or stops – even if the other factors are in abundant supply. The greater the rate of photosynthesis, the greater the growth rate of plants. Therefore, if limiting factors slow the rate of photosynthesis then the growth rate of the plants affected also slows.

Synoptic link

See Topic 11.1, Overview of photosynthesis, Topic 11.2, The light-dependent reaction, and Topic 12.1, Glycolysis.

Reviewing Topic 1.2, Carbohydrates: monosaccharides will remind you of triose and hexose sugars.

When carbon dioxide is in short supply, the rate of conversion of RuBP to GP in the light-independent reaction decreases. As a result, RuBP builds up and triose sugar is not produced.

At low temperature, the number of collisions between enzyme and substrate molecules decreases. As a result, the rate of the enzyme-catalysed reactions producing triose sugar during the light-independent reaction decreases.

At low light intensity, the production of ATP and reduced NADP in the light-dependent reaction decreases (stops). As a result, GP is not converted into triose sugar during the light-independent reaction, GP builds up, and RuBP is used up.

These effects of limiting factors reduce the rate of photosynthesis and therefore slow the rate of plant growth.

Photolysis literally means 'breaking down by light'.

Question and model answer

Q What are the biochemical outcomes of the light-dependent reaction?

A The photolysis of water releases protons (H^+), electrons (e^-), and oxygen gas.

ATP and reduced NADP are produced and available in the light-independent reaction where carbon dioxide is reduced, forming triose sugar.

Summary questions

1 How is NADP regenerated in the light-independent reaction? (*4 marks*)

2 What is meant by the statement 'the combination of two molecules of TP produces a molecule of glucose by reverse glycolysis'? (*4 marks*)

Chapter 11 Practice questions

Between 1946 and 1953 Melvin Calvin and his team at the University of California at Berkley investigated the biochemistry of photosynthesis. In particular they turned their attention to the details of the light-independent reactions. The work depended on using the radioactive isotope of carbon ^{14}C which had just become available for research work.

Calvin grew cultures of the photoautrophic protist *Chlorella* in a transparent container – the so-called 'lollipop' apparatus. Figure 1 illustrates the set up. The *Chlorella* culture was illuminated and, with photosynthesis underway, was exposed to radioactively labelled sodium hydrogencarbonate (NaH^{14}CO$_3$). The labelled hydrogencarbonate ion (H^{14}CO$_3^-$) was fixed by the *Chlorella* to become part of the light-independent reaction. Samples of the culture were run off at regular intervals (5, 10, 15, 20 … seconds after exposure of the *Chlorella* to the radioactive isotope and the start of photosynthesis) into hot ethanol, which killed the cells. The mixture was concentrated and the products of the light-independent reaction as photosynthesis got underway were separated using the recently developed technique of two-dimensional chromatography.

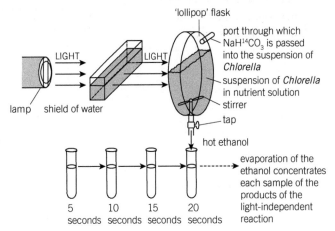

▲ Figure 1

Calvin reasoned that if the light-independent reactions by which carbon dioxide is reduced to make carbohydrate form a series, then by stopping the reactions at known intervals after the introduction of labelled carbon dioxide into the *Chlorella* culture, it should be possible to find the intermediate compounds in the process.

Using chromatography and autoradiography, Calvin and his co-workers traced the pathway of ^{14}C through a variety of intermediate compounds. Figure 2 illustrates some of their results.

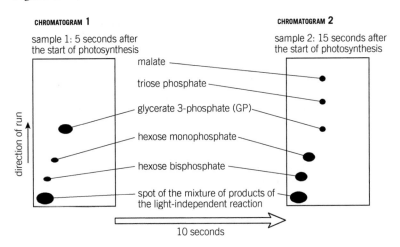

▲ Figure 2

1 Explain the role of the radioactive isotope ^{14}C and two-dimensional chromatography in Calvin's work. *(4 marks)*

2 In Figure 1, why were samples of the culture run off from the lollipop apparatus at 5-second intervals after exposure of the *Chlorella* to the radioactive isotope and the start of photosynthesis? *(5 marks)*

3 In Figure 1, explain the importance of the water shield in the experiment. *(2 marks)*

4 Describe the differences between chromatogram 1 and chromatogram 2. *(3 marks)*

5 What do the differences between chromatogram 1 and chromatogram 2 suggest? *(2 marks)*

12.1 Glycolysis

Specification reference: 3.5.2

Glycolysis: the sequence of reactions

Glycolysis is the first stage of **cellular respiration**. It occurs in the cytoplasm of cells whether oxygen is abundant (**aerobic** conditions) or in short supply (**anaerobic** conditions). Its reactions begin the oxidation of glucose. Energy is released and ATP is made.

Glycolysis

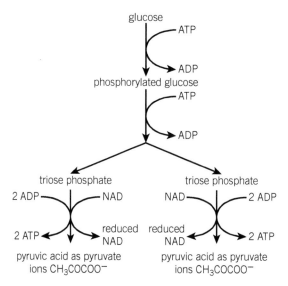

▲ **Figure 1** *Glycolysis: the sequence*

- A glucose molecule is phosphorylated. The reaction is endothermic and makes the glucose molecule more reactive. The energy comes from the hydrolysis of ATP providing a phosphate group which binds to the glucose molecule.

$$ATP \longrightarrow ADP + P_i$$

Phosphorylation commits the glucose molecule to enter the sequence of reactions of glycolysis.

- Further phosphorylation occurs. The reaction is endothermic and the addition of another phosphate group makes the molecule even more reactive. Another molecule of ATP is used up. Remember that molecules of glucose and fructose each contain 6 carbon atoms.

- The twice phosphorylated molecule splits into two molecules of phosphorylated triose sugar, which in turn are converted in a series of reactions to pyruvate ions (you are not expected to remember the details).

The reactions are exothermic.

- Four phosphate groups are transferred from the molecules of triose sugar to ADP, forming four molecules of ATP (two molecules for each of triose sugar). The process is called **substrate-level phosphorylation**.

- At the same time, the triose sugars are oxidised. Two pairs of hydrogen atoms (one pair for each molecule of triose sugar) are released. The loss of hydrogen by each molecule of triose sugar is an example of a dehydrogenation reaction. Each pair of hydrogen atoms is transferred to a molecule of the hydrogen acceptor **nicotinamide adenine dinucleotide** (NAD), forming reduced NAD.

- The formation of pyruvate ions marks the completion of glycolysis.

12.2 Link reaction and Krebs cycle

Specification reference: 3.5.2

Aerobic respiration

The reactions of aerobic respiration occur in the mitochondria. Some of the energy released during the reactions is stored in molecules of ATP.

How is ATP produced during aerobic respiration?

During aerobic respiration ATP is produced from two sources:

- **Substrate-level phosphorylation** – a type of chemical reaction where ATP is produced by the direct transfer of a phosphate group to ADP from another reactive substance. It occurs in the presence or absence of oxygen.

- **Oxidative phosphorylation** – electrons are released during the reactions of glycolysis, the link reaction, and the Krebs cycle. The electrons are accepted by the coenzymes **NAD** and **FAD**, producing reduced NAD and FAD respectively. Ultimately the electrons are transferred from reduced NAD and FAD to oxygen which serves as the final electron acceptor. During the transfer of electrons, energy is released and ATP is produced. Oxidative phosphorylation occurs only in the presence of oxygen.

For each molecule of glucose entering glycolysis, two pyruvate ions are produced. In aerobic conditions, pyruvate is taken up by mitochondria. Its uptake is by active transport and uses ATP.

Synoptic link

See Topic 12.1, Glycolysis to remind you that glycolysis comes before the link reaction and Krebs cycle.

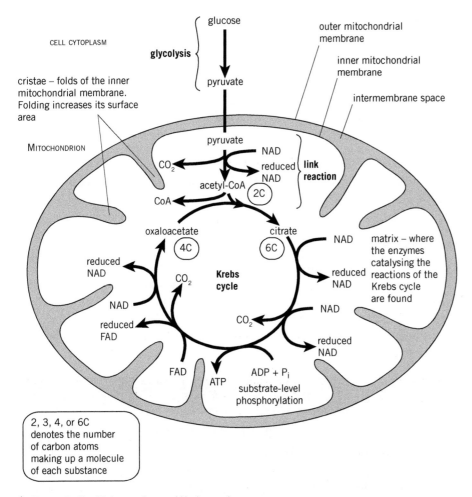

▲ **Figure 1** *The Link reaction and Krebs cycle*

Synoptic link

See Topic 12.1, Glycolysis.

Revision tip

Respiratory substrates that enter the Krebs cycle include the breakdown products of lipids and amino acids.

Key terms

Decarboxylation: A reaction where a carboxyl group $(-COO^- + H^+)$ is removed from a substance. Carbon dioxide is produced.

Dehydrogenation: A reaction where hydrogen atoms are removed from a substance.

Coenzyme: A molecule which binds to an atom (or group of atoms) of one molecule and transfers the atom (or group of atoms) to another molecule. NAD and FAD are examples, as well as NADP, which is produced in the light-dependent reaction of photosynthesis, and used in the light-independent reaction (Calvin cycle).

Revision tip

Remember that glycolysis occurs whether oxygen is abundant (aerobic conditions) or in short supply (anaerobic conditions).

In a mitochondrion, the pyruvate ions enter the link reaction, which couples glycolysis with the reactions of the Krebs cycle. See Figure 1 for details of the link reaction and the Krebs cycle.

The link reaction and the Krebs cycle

- Pyruvate passes into a mitochondrion where it is oxidised by the removal of hydrogen atoms, which are transferred to NAD to produce reduced NAD. The removal of hydrogen atoms is another example of a dehydrogenation reaction catalysed by **dehydrogenase** enzymes.
- A molecule of carbon dioxide is also released. The release is another example of a decarboxylation reaction catalysed by **decarboxylase** enzymes.

As a result **3-carbon** pyruvate is converted to a **2-carbon** acetyl group.

- The acetyl group formed combines with coenzyme A (CoA), producing **acetyl coenzyme A** (abbreviated as acetyl CoA).

The formation of acetyl CoA couples glycolysis with the Krebs cycle: the so-called **link reaction**.

- The acetyl group containing 2 carbon atoms carried by CoA is transferred to the **4-carbon** compound **oxaloacetic acid** (as oxaloacetate ions). The coenzyme A is released.

As a result the **6-carbon** compound **citric acid** (as citrate ions) is formed.

- A cyclic sequence of reactions follows, during which 2 carbon atoms, each from a different compound in the sequence, are removed in the form of carbon dioxide, CO_2. Each removal is an example of a decarboxylation reaction catalysed by a decarboxylase enzyme.
- Also pairs of hydrogen atoms are removed, each pair from a particular compound in the sequence of reactions. Each removal is yet another example of a dehydrogenation reaction catalysed by a dehydrogenase enzyme.

The hydrogen atoms combine with either NAD or FAD, producing reduced NAD or FAD, respectively.

- ATP is produced by substrate-level phosphorylation.
- The formation of 4-carbon compound oxaloacetate marks the completion of the Krebs cycle. The next sequence of reactions begins with the reaction of oxaloacetate with acetyl CoA, forming 6-carbon compound citrate.

What happens next?

Hydrogen atoms removed from compounds produced by the breakdown of respiratory substrates (e.g. glucose) during glycolysis, the link reaction, and the Krebs cycle are transferred ultimately as electrons (e^-) and protons (H^+) to oxygen, forming water. The transfer of electrons is by a series of **redox** reactions along a chain of electron acceptor molecules called the **electron transfer chain**.

Summary questions

1 What is the difference between a dehydrogenation and decarboxylation reaction? *(2 marks)*

2 What is the role of acetyl CoA in aerobic respiration? *(2 marks)*

3 In which organelle of a cell, and in what part of the organelle, do the reactions of the Krebs cycle take place? *(2 marks)*

12.3 Oxidative phosphorylation

Specification reference: 3.5.2

Electron transfer and proton pumping

Oxidative phosphorylation is so called because:

- the combination of ADP and P_i making ATP is a phosphorylation reaction
- oxygen is required as the final electron acceptor of the electron transport chain of proteins and coenzymes (labelled **A** to **D** and **x** and **y** respectively in Figure 1 below).

Figure 1 shows you where oxidative phosphorylation of ADP forming ATP takes place in the mitochondrion.

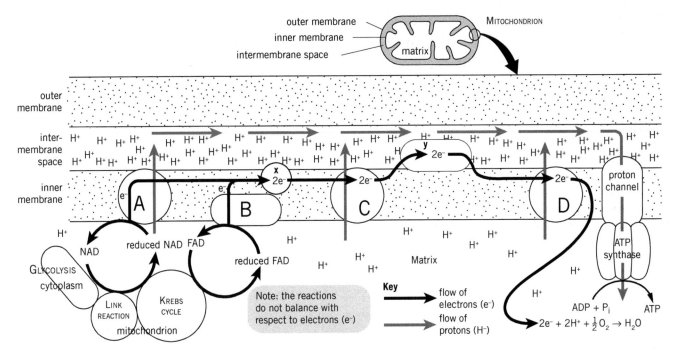

▲ **Figure 1** *Electron transfer (transport) chain*

Transferring electrons

- During glycolysis, the link reaction, and the Krebs cycle, oxidation reactions remove hydrogen atoms from different compounds as electrons and protons.
- The reactions are coupled to the electron transfer chain by the electron acceptors NAD and FAD.
- When NAD and FAD accept electrons they are reduced.
- Reduced NAD transfers electrons to protein **A** in Figure 1.

As a result of the transfer, reduced NAD is oxidised to NAD and protein **A** is reduced.

- Electrons are transferred from reduced protein **A** to protein **C** by way of coenzyme **x**.

As a result, reduced protein **A** is re-oxidised and protein **C** reduced.

- Electrons are also transferred from reduced FAD as part of protein **B** to protein **C** by way of coenzyme **x**.

As a result, reduced FAD is oxidised to FAD and protein **C** is further reduced.

- Electrons are then transferred from reduced protein **C** to protein **D** by way of coenzyme **y**.

As a result, reduced protein **C** is re-oxidised and protein **D** reduced.

- Electrons from reduced protein **D** are transferred with protons to oxygen. Molecules of water form and reduced protein **D** is re-oxidised, marking the end reaction of the electron transfer chain.

Pumping protons

The redox reactions of the electron transfer chain release energy, which enables proteins **A**, **C**, and **D** to pump protons from the mitochondrial matrix across the inner mitochondrial membrane into the mitochondrial intermembrane space.

As a result, protons accumulate in the intermembrane space. (*Remember:* Protons carry a positive charge (H^+).) So a proton gradient develops across the inner mitochondrial membrane.

- The potential difference across the inner mitochondrial membrane is $-200\,mV$ (the charge on the matrix side of the membrane is more negative than the side of the membrane facing the intermembrane space).
- The difference in charge results in an electrochemical gradient (of protons) and represents a store of energy.

Synthesising ATP

Proton channels consisting of different proteins are part of the inner mitochondrial membrane. Each pore consists of:

- channel proteins which pass from the side of the membrane facing the intermembrane space to the matrix side of the membrane
- the enzyme ATP synthase, which is connected by a stalk to the channel proteins and projects into the matrix of the mitochondrion.

Protons accumulated in the intermembrane space diffuse down the proton gradient from the intermembrane space through the channel proteins and ATP synthase to the matrix. This is called **chemiosmosis**.

- As a result, energy is released and ADP combines with P_i. The reaction is catalysed by ATP synthase. ATP is formed (oxidative phosphorylation).

Synoptic link

See Topic 2.3, Energy and ATP, Topic 4.1, Structure of the cell-surface membrane, Topic 12.1, Glycolysis, and Topic 12.2, Link reaction and Krebs cycle.

Common misconception: How much ATP?

In theory, the oxidation of a molecule of reduced NAD to NAD releases enough energy to charge the electrochemical gradient of protons (see Pumping protons, above) with enough potential to generate 3 ATP molecules.

Similarly, the oxidation of a molecule of reduced FAD to FAD releases energy with the potential of generating 2 ATP molecules. However, it seems that reduced NAD and FAD generate only about 2.5 and 1.5 ATP molecules, respectively, because not all of the energy stored in the proton gradient is available to generate ATP. For example, the active transport of pyruvate ions into mitochondria from the cell's cytoplasm consumes ATP.

Summary questions

1 Cyanide is a poison. It binds with protein **D** of the electron transport chain shown in Figure 1, preventing the transport of protons (H^+) from the mitochondrial matrix into the intermembrane space. Explain why a person who ingests (takes in) cyanide might die.   (*5 marks*)

2 Summarise the process and the outcome of chemiosmosis.   (*10 marks*)

12.4 Anaerobic respiration

Specification reference: 3.5.2

When oxygen is in short supply

Glycolysis is the first stage of cellular respiration. In:

- **aerobic conditions** – pyruvate ions pass to Krebs cycle via the link reaction.

- **anaerobic conditions (when oxygen is in short supply)** – pyruvate ions undergo a process of fermentation.

Two of the most common types are lactic acid fermentation (muscle cells) and alcohol fermentation (yeast cells). Figure 1 is your guide to the reactions.

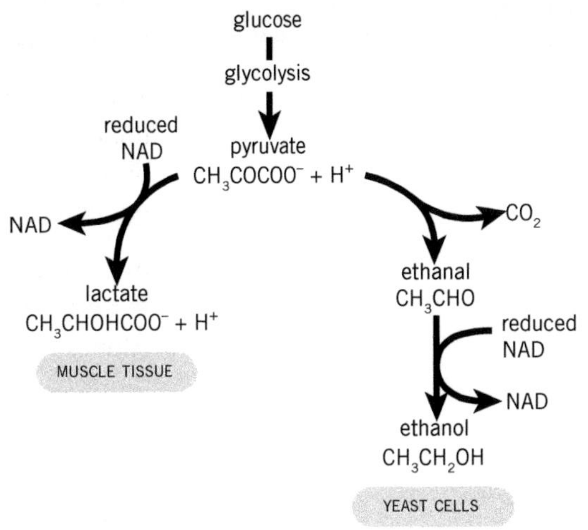

In human muscle tissue

- Pyruvate produced by glycolysis in anaerobic conditions accumulates more rapidly than can be processed via the Krebs cycle.

- Oxidation of reduced NAD transfers hydrogen atoms to pyruvate, reducing it.

As a result lactate ($CH_3CHOHCOO^- + H^+$) is formed, pyruvate does not accumulate during glycolysis, and NAD is regenerated and is available to accept more hydrogen atoms.

Regeneration of NAD is required if glycolysis is to continue. Without it, glycolysis would stop. As a result, ATP would not be produced by substrate-level phosphorylation during glycolysis. When more oxygen becomes available, lactate either:

- undergoes reverse glycolysis, synthesising molecules of glucose, or

- enters the Krebs cycle where it is oxidised, forming carbon dioxide and water.

The amount of oxygen required to metabolize excess lactate is called the **oxygen debt**.

▲ **Figure 1** *Types of fermentation reaction*

In yeast cells

- Pyruvate produced by glycolysis in anaerobic conditions accumulates more rapidly than it can be processed via the Krebs cycle.

- The carboxyl group ($-COO^-$) of pyruvate is removed as carbon dioxide. This is another example of **decarboxylation** catalysed by the **decarboxylase** enzyme.

As a result, ethanal (CH_3CHO) is formed.

- Oxidation of reduced NAD transfers hydrogen atoms to ethanal, reducing it.

As a result, ethanol (CH_3CH_2OH) is formed, pyruvate does not accumulate during glycolysis, and NAD is regenerated and available to accept more hydrogen atoms.

- Regeneration of NAD is required if glycolysis is to continue. Without it glycolysis would stop.

As a result, ATP would not be produced by substrate-level phosphorylation during glycolysis.

Synoptic link

Topic 12.1, Glycolysis, shows that glycolysis occurs in anaerobic conditions as well as aerobic conditions.

Comparing ATP yields

When a molecule of glucose is completely oxidised in the reactions of aerobic respiration, 40 molecules of ATP are produced. However the net yield of ATP molecules per molecule of glucose is 38 because two molecules of ATP are used in glycolysis.

This net yield represents about 40% of the potential energy contained in a molecule of glucose. The remaining 60% of energy is released as heat. In birds and mammals, the high rate of cellular respiration is the source of heat which enables them to maintain constant body temperature.

In anaerobic conditions, only the reactions of glycolysis take place. 4 molecules of ATP are produced by substrate-level phosphorylation. However, 2 molecules are used in glycolysis. Therefore the net gain of ATP molecules available following respiration in anaerobic conditions is only 2.

Summary questions

1 How is NAD regenerated in muscle cells respiring anaerobically?

(*2 marks*)

2 What is the difference in the regeneration of NAD in yeast cells and muscle cells respiring anaerobically? (*3 marks*)

3 What is oxygen debt? (*3 marks*)

Chapter 12 Practice questions

1 The rate of photosynthesis determines the growth rate of plants. Limiting factors affect the rate of photosynthesis and therefore affect growth rate.

   a Describe the limiting factors of photosynthesis. (*3 marks*)

   b Explain how a greenhouse might reduce the effects of limiting factors on the growth rate of plants. (*2 marks*)

2

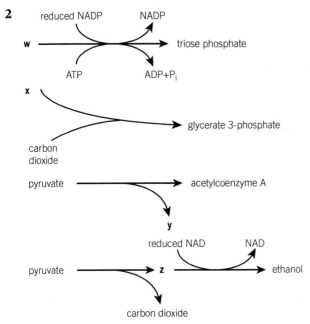

The diagrams show some of the reactions that occur during photosynthesis and cellular respiration.

Name the compounds labelled **w**, **x**, **y**, and **z**. (*4 marks*)

3 Cyanide is a poison. It binds with one of the proteins in the electron transport chain. Lactate accumulates in cells as the result of cyanide poisoning.

   a Explain the effect of cyanide poisoning on ATP synthesis. (*3 marks*)

   b Explain why lactate accumulates as the result of cyanide poisoning. (*3 marks*)

Food

All of the places on Earth where there is life form the biosphere. An ecosystem is a part of the biosphere where the populations of organisms living in a particular environment are characteristic of that ecosystem and not other ecosystems. A pond, coral reef, and tropical rain forest are examples of ecosystems.

An ecosystem works through the interactions between its populations of organisms. Food is an important component of these interactions. Describing feeding relationships between its populations shows how food is transferred between organisms and is one way of how an ecosystem works.

Transferring food: food chains and food webs

Different words are used to describe the feeding relationships between the populations of an ecosystem.

- **Producers** make food (sugars). Plants are producers. So too are some types of single-celled organisms and algae. Most of them make food by **photosynthesis**. Food chains and food webs always begin with producers.

- **Consumers** take in food (feeding) already made. Animals and decomposers are consumers.

A food chain shows the links between producers and consumers. It describes one pathway of food through an ecosystem. For example:

oak leaves → slugs → thrush → sparrowhawk

Transferring food: trophic levels

Food chains and food webs represent the feeding relationships of ecosystems but do not indicate the numbers or mass of individuals involved. The description is *qualitative*. Ecological pyramids represent a *quantitative* description of feeding relationships. They describe how much food is transferred through the community (see Figure 1).

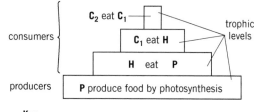

Key
P = plants H = herbivores C_1 = first carnivores
C_2 = second carnivores

▲ **Figure 1** *An ecological pyramid*

Organisms with similar types of food are grouped into trophic (feeding) levels.

- The producer trophic level occupies the base of the pyramid.
- Other trophic levels are made up of consumers:
  - primary consumers are herbivores (H)
  - secondary consumers or first/primary carnivores (C1) feed on herbivores
  - tertiary consumers or second/secondary carnivores (C2) feed on first/primary carnivores.

There are different types of ecological pyramid.

Transferring energy between organisms

Sunlight underpins the existence of most of life on Earth. Without sunlight and the producers which convert its energy into food energy, food chains and food webs would collapse. Most ecosystems would not exist.

Key term

Food web: Describes all possible feeding relationships of an ecosystem. It consists of interlinked food chains.

Revision tip
Fragments of dead material (e.g. twigs, leaves) form detritus. Animals that feed on detritus are called **detritivores**.

Light energy is trapped and converted by most producers into the chemical bond energy of sugars (food) by the reactions of photosynthesis. Energy is transferred through food chains and food webs, and between trophic levels, when consumers feed on producers and one another. See Figure 2. In other words, **feeding** transfers food energy from producers to consumers.

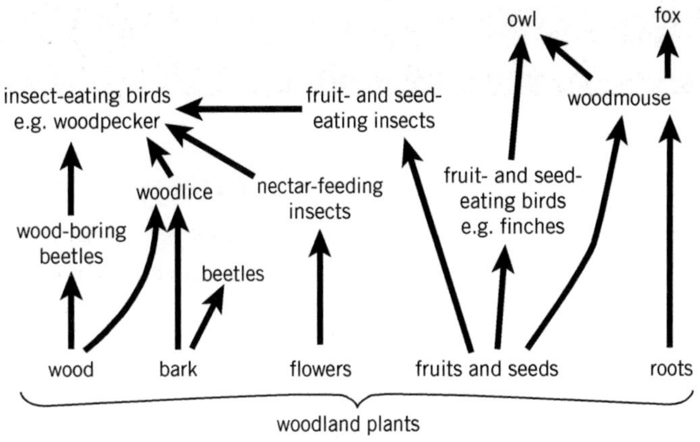

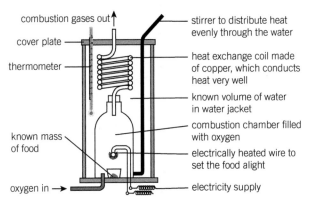

▲ **Figure 2** *A food web*

Measuring food energy

- The biomass of an area is measured as the dry mass of living organisms per square metre at a given time. The energy stored in dry mass can be estimated using calorimetry. The energy value of food (of known dry biomass) is measured using an instrument called a **bomb calorimeter**. Figure 3 shows the setup.

Diagram labels (left to right):
combustion gases out
cover plate
thermometer
known mass of food
oxygen in →

stirrer to distribute heat evenly through the water
heat exchange coil made of copper, which conducts heat very well
known volume of water in water jacket
combustion chamber filled with oxygen
electrically heated wire to set the food alight
electricity supply

▲ **Figure 3** *A bomb calorimeter is made to reduce the loss of heat to the surroundings, and maximise the transfer of heat from the burning food to the water in the water jacket. In this way, the accuracy of the data on the energy values of foods burnt in the calorimeter is improved*

Note that:

- Food (dry mass) is burnt in an oxygen-rich atmosphere, ensuring complete combustion. The burning food releases food energy as heat.
- The heat exchange coil transfers heat released by the burning food to the water in the surrounding water jacket.

The data and how to use it

- The temperature of the water in the water jacket is measured before and after the food is burnt.
- The rise in temperature is calculated.
- The change in temperature is used to work out the energy value per unit mass (e.g. 1 g, 100 g) of food:

$$\text{Energy released per gram of food} = \frac{\text{volume in water in water jacket} \times \text{temperature rise} \times 4.2}{\text{mass of food}}$$

Decomposers

Decomposers are called **saprobionts**. Fungi and bacteria are decomposers. They are consumers that obtain food (energy) by breaking down dead organisms. Breakdown occurs because decomposers release enzymes onto dead remains. The enzymes catalyse the digestion of the dead organic material. The products of digestion are absorbed by the decomposers and are a source of energy to them.

The transfer of energy through decomposers and detritivores is often left out of diagrams representing food chains, food webs, and ecological pyramids. Remember, however, that in some communities, 80% of the productivity of a trophic level may flow through decomposer food chains.

Revision tip

The energy released per unit mass of food depends on the nutrients it contains. Typical energy values for different nutrients are:

carbohydrates 17.2 kJ g^{-1}

proteins 22.2 kJ g^{-1}

lipids 38.5 kJ g^{-1}

Synoptic link

Referring to Topic 19.1, Populations and ecosystems and Topic 19.2, Variation in population size will remind you of the relationship between an ecosystem and its populations.

Summary questions

1 What is a trophic level?
(*2 marks*)

2 List the different types of consumer and briefly explain what each type eats. (*4 marks*)

Energy transfer between trophic levels

Figure 1 tracks the transfer of energy between trophic levels:
producer → herbivore → carnivore.

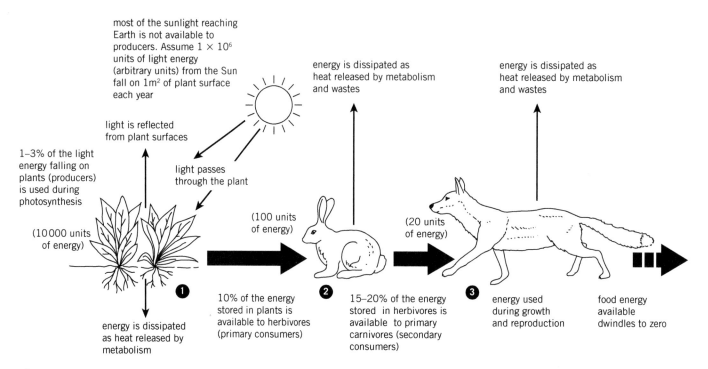

most of the sunlight reaching Earth is not available to producers. Assume 1×10^6 units of light energy (arbitrary units) from the Sun fall on 1m² of plant surface each year

energy is dissipated as heat released by metabolism and wastes

energy is dissipated as heat released by metabolism and wastes

light is reflected from plant surfaces

1–3% of the light energy falling on plants (producers) is used during photosynthesis

light passes through the plant

(10000 units of energy)

(100 units of energy)

(20 units of energy)

①

energy is dissipated as heat released by metabolism

② 10% of the energy stored in plants is available to herbivores (primary consumers)

15–20% of the energy stored in herbivores is available to primary carnivores (secondary consumers)

③ energy used during growth and reproduction

food energy available dwindles to zero

▲ **Figure 1** *Transferring energy*

1 Energy is not available because some parts of plants may not be palatable (e.g. bitter tasting leaves) or accessible (e.g. roots) to herbivores although counting towards the overall energy content of producers. As a result, the parts are not eaten and therefore do not count as energy available to herbivores.

2 Animals do not produce enzymes that digest cellulose and lignin. As a result, plant material is difficult to digest. Herbivores produce a large amount of faeces, which contain undigested plant material, representing energy not available to carnivores.

3 Animal material is easier to digest than plant material and has a higher energy content. As a result the transfer of energy from herbivore to carnivore is more efficient (20%) than from producer to herbivore (5–10%).

Energy is lost from the food chain to the environment at each stage of energy transfer between the Sun and trophic levels. As a result when food energy dwindles to zero, organisms cannot exist. This means that the number of trophic levels in an ecological pyramid and links in a food chain or web are limited.

Productivity

Productivity is:

- the rate at which biomass is produced in grams (g) or kilograms (kg) per unit area (cm²/m²) of plant surface (depending on the size of plant) per unit time (e.g. year⁻¹)

or

- **the volume** (cm³/m³) of photosynthetic tissues produced (depending on the size of plant) per unit time (e.g. year⁻¹).

Revision tip

The indigestible parts of prey (hooves, hides, bones) represent energy not available to other carnivores.

Key terms

Gross primary production (GPP): The biomass of organic material (food) produced in g m⁻² unit time⁻¹, or m⁻³ unit time⁻¹.

Net primary production (NPP): The GPP less the biomass used by producers to fuel their own metabolism (losses to the environment through respiration (R) account for 20–50% of producer GPP).

Losses to the environment

$$NPP = GPP - R$$

The net production of consumers is measured as the increase in their body mass (growth) as the result of consuming food. However, not all of the energy content of food is available for growth. Losses to the environment include respiration, excretion of urine, and the removal of faeces (see Figure 1).

$$N = I - (F + R)$$

Where

N = net production,

I = energy content of ingested food,

F = energy content of faeces and urine lost to the environment,

R = energy in respiration lost to the environment.

Synoptic link

Referring to Topic 11.1, Overview of photosynthesis, will remind you that productivity depends on the rate of photosynthesis.

Summary questions

1 How does the description of the flow of energy through the community help us understand why there is a limited number of links in a food chain? *(3 marks)*

2 Explain why it is difficult for animals to digest plant material. *(4 marks)*

3 Suggest why the productivity of tropical rain forests is greater than temperate grasslands. *(3 marks)*

4 In terms of the energy content of the food we eat, explain why a vegetarian diet is more energy efficient than a diet that includes meat. *(3 marks)*

13.3 Nutrient cycles

Specification reference: 3.5.4

Features of nutrient cycles

The compounds formed from carbon, nitrogen, phosphorus, and other elements taken from the environment by producers and transferred to consumers through food chains, are nutrients essential for healthy life. When organisms die, the nutrients are released back into the environment by the

- physical processes of climate
- biochemical processes of respiration and photosynthesis
- saprobiontic activities of bacteria and fungi.

The above are common features of all nutrient cycles.

Fungi and bacteria are called **saprobionts** because they feed on dead organic matter. Their feeding activities cause decomposition which is why they are also called **decomposers**. Their activities recycle nutrients between organisms and the environment.

The nitrogen cycle

- Nitrogen is the most abundant gas in the atmosphere.

  Most organisms *cannot* use gaseous nitrogen directly.

- Some types of bacteria called **nitrogen-fixing** bacteria have **nitrogenase** enzymes which catalyse the combination of gaseous nitrogen with hydrogen, forming ammonia (NH_3). In solution, ammonia forms ammonium ions (NH_4^+).
  Some plants take up ammonium ions in solution through their roots (plants also take up nitrate ions in solution), enabling them to synthesise nucleic acids and proteins.

  Feeding transfers nitrogen (as nitrogen-containing compounds) from producers to consumers through food chains.

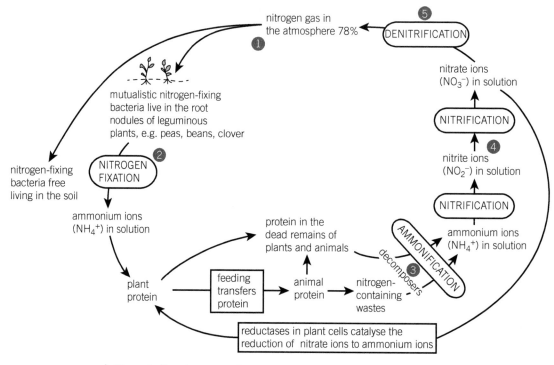

▲ **Figure 1** *The nitrogen cycle*

- **Ammonification** refers to the enzyme-catalysed reactions which break down dead organisms and nitrogen containing wastes. A variety of decomposers are responsible.
- As a result ammonium ions (NH_4^+) are formed.
- **Nitrification** refers to the oxidation reactions carried out by **nitrifying bacteria**. The reactions convert ammonium (NH_4^+) compounds to nitrites (NO_2^-) and then to nitrates (NO_3^-).

As a result, nitrogen as nitrates (NO_3^-) is available in a form that is most easily absorbed by the roots of plants.

Common misconception: Nitrates → Nitrites → Ammonium ions

You should not forget that nitrate ions, when absorbed by plant cells, are first reduced to nitrite ions and then to ammonium ions before becoming part of nucleic acids, proteins, and other nitrogen-containing compounds.

- **Denitrification** refers to the reduction reactions carried out by **denitrifying bacteria**. The reactions occur in anaerobic conditions and convert nitrate ions (NO_3^-) to nitrogen gas (N_2).

As a result, nitrogen gas enters the atmosphere.

The phosphorus cycle

The element phosphorus is an important component of ATP and nucleic acids. The atmosphere is the major reservoir of nitrogen. Rock (not the atmosphere) is the major reservoir of phosphorus, mostly as phosphate ions (PO_4^{3-}).

- The physical processes of the climate (weathering) release phosphate ions from rocks.
- Phosphate ions pass to the environment (soil and water).
- Producers absorb phosphate ions from the environment.
- Phosphate ions transfer to consumers through food chains.
- When producers and consumers die, decomposition as the result of the feeding activities of fungi and bacteria (decomposers) releases phosphate ions into the environment.
- Therefore, phosphate ions are recycled and available for:
  - absorption by new generations of producers
  - transfer from producers to consumers.

Revision tip

Decomposition is the result of enzymes secreted by decomposers (fungi and bacteria) catalysing reactions that break down dead organic matter. Some of the breakdown products are absorbed by the decomposers. The rest are released into the environment, and are nutrients essential for the growth of producers.

Synoptic link

Referring to Topic 19.1, Populations and ecosystems reminds you of how nutrients are recycled in the environment.

Summary questions

1 Outline the stages in the phosphorus cycle and nitrogen cycle and compare them. *(6 marks)*

2 Why are fields sown with leguminous crops (e.g. peas and beans) in 'rotation' with other crops? *(3 marks)*

13.4 Use of natural and artificial fertilisers

Enriching the soil

Farms are ecosystems with people as consumers in a food chain of crops and livestock. Intensive farming refers to the different methods used to increase productivity. In other words, the aim is to maximise the amount of food produced. Spreading fertilisers on fields growing crops and pasture grazing livestock is one of the methods used to increase productivity.

Why are fertilisers needed?

The growth (and therefore productivity) of crops and pasture-grazing livestock depends on the elements and compounds (nutrients) that occur naturally in soil. Substances that add nutrients to soil are called **fertilisers**. They help to increase productivity by replacing the nutrients that crops and pasture take from the soil during the growing season and that are not replaced because crops are removed from the lands when harvested. In addition, livestock eat the plants (usually grass) that make up pasture and are then taken off the land and sent to market.

How do fertilisers increase productivity?

Table 1 lists the ions of some of the elements that crops need in relatively large amounts, **macronutrients**.

▼ **Table 1** *Important macronutrients*

Nutrient	ppm*	Ion	% of crop dry mass	Requirement
Nitrogen	15 000	NO_3^-	3.5	Synthesis of amino acids, proteins, and nucleic acids
Potassium	10 000	K^+	3.4	Enzyme co-factor, opening of stomata
Calcium	5000	Ca^{2+}	0.7	Formation of the plant cell wall
Phosphorus	2000	PO_4^{3-}	0.4	Synthesis of ATP and nucleic acids
Magnesium	2000	Mg^{2+}	0.1	Synthesis of chlorophyll
Sulphur	1000	SO_4^{2-}	0.1	Synthesis of some amino acids

*ppm = parts per million in solution

The ions of other elements are needed by plants in much smaller amounts (measured in tens of ppm or less). Many of them act as enzyme cofactors. The column in Table 1 headed 'Requirement' lists why the different elements, and the ions containing them, are important for plant growth (and therefore productivity). For example, the synthesis of amino acids and proteins adds to the biomass of crops. Chlorophyll maximises the capture of light energy and therefore the rate at which crops photosynthesise biomass (sugars).

Natural versus artificial

Natural fertilisers (organic material such as manure and compost) are spread on soil. They help to maintain its structure. Fungi and bacteria decompose the material, releasing nutrients, which are absorbed by crops.

Manure consists of the faeces (often mixed with bedding straw) of farm animals. The dung is collected and left to decay before spreading over fields. Compost consists of vegetable scraps, garden waste, and plant cuttings collected in a heap. Decomposers (bacteria and fungi) break it down, releasing nutrients to the soil, making them available for absorption by, and the growth of, new plants. Artificial fertilisers are a product of the agrochemical industry. They are added to soil as sprays or granules. Most artificial fertilisers supply nitrogen (N), phosphorus (P), and potassium (K) – the so called **NPK fertilisers**.

13.5 Environmental issues concerning use of nitrogen-containing fertilisers

Specification reference: 3.5.4

Eutrophication

NPK fertilisers are very soluble in water. They **leach** from the soil into rivers, lakes, and the sea. People produce sewage which (treated and untreated) passes into rivers and the sea. Sewage is rich in nitrogen- and phosphorus-containing compounds.

NPK fertilisers and sewage are a source of nutrients for bacteria and other microorganisms living in water. As the water becomes richer and richer in the nutrients, the aquatic (living in water) plants and algae, and microorganisms rapidly increase in numbers. This process is called **eutrophication**.

Growth of aquatic plants and algae increases. Single-celled algae multiply, covering the water's surface (algal bloom). As a result:

- Light is prevented from penetrating beneath the water's surface. Aquatic plants beneath the water's surface are deprived of light, and therefore there is no photosynthesis.
- The plants die and dead organic material accumulates. Aerobic bacteria decompose the dead organic material.
- Because of the increasing activity of aerobic bacteria, more oxygen in solution is used up (increasing biological oxygen demand, BOD).
- The concentration of dissolved oxygen decreases. Fish, and other organisms requiring a high concentration of dissolved oxygen, die and the accumulation of dead organic material increases.
- Anaerobic bacteria continue the decomposition of dead organic material and only those species of organism able to tolerate the reduced concentration of dissolved oxygen survive.
- The populations of these species increases.

The more NPK fertilisers and sewage in solution, the less the concentration of oxygen. As a result, there are a smaller number of species surviving in the polluted water, and biodiversity is reduced even though the numbers of a particular species increase. The presence or absence of different species indicates how polluted the water is with fertiliser; these species are called **indicator species**.

> **Key term**
>
> **Leaching:** Removing substances in solution

> **Key term**
>
> **Biological oxygen demand, BOD:** The uptake of oxygen in solution by microorganisms living in water increases as bacteria and algae multiply, this is an increase in BOD.

> **Key term**
>
> **Biodiversity:** The number of species in an ecosystem.

> **Synoptic link**
>
> Referring to Topic 13.2, Energy transfer and productivity and Topic 13.4, Use of natural and artificial fertilisers, reminds you of their link to environmental pollution.

Summary questions

1 Outline the process of eutrophication.   (*8 marks*)

2 What is an indicator species?   (*3 marks*)
3 Algae multiply rapidly in nutrient-rich water, producing an algal bloom. Explain why.   (*3 marks*)

1 For every $1\,m^2$ of grass it eats, a cow obtains $3000\,kJ$ of energy. It uses $100\,kJ$ in growth, $1000\,kJ$ are lost as body heat, and $1900\,kJ$ are lost in faeces.

   a What percentage of the energy in $1\,m^2$ of grass is used in growth? *(2 marks)*

   b Food passes through its gut. What percentage of the energy in $1\,m^2$ of grass is not absorbed? *(2 marks)*

   c If beef has an energy value of $12\,kJ\,g^{-1}$, how many m^2 of grass are needed to produce $100\,g$ of beef? *(2 marks)*

2 For a farm of 640 hectares, the energy input of the Sun received at ground level $= 0.35\ MJ\,cm^{-2}\,year^{-1}$ (100 million $cm^2 = 1$ hectare).

   a Calculate the value of the Sun's energy input for the farm as a whole. *(2 marks)*

   b Combine your answer to part **a** with the following data and calculate the amount of light energy converted into crop biomass each year.

   ○ Photosynthetic efficiency $= 0.8\%$

   $$\left(\text{photosynthetic efficiency} = \frac{\text{energy content of plants}}{\text{light energy available per year}}\right)$$

   ○ Average crop cover $= 50\%$

   ○ Length of time crops cover the soil each year $= 6$ months *(4 marks)*

14.1 Survival and response

Specification reference: 3.6.1.1

Stimuli and responses

The contraction of muscles pulling on a skeleton enables animals to respond to stimuli. Plant responses are the result of growth movements. When plant movements are the result of **directional stimuli** (stimuli coming mainly from one direction), then the response is called a **tropism**. Tropisms are the result of differences in the growth rate of tissues on one side or the other of the shoots or roots in question.

Tropisms are **positive** if a plant grows towards the more intense source of a stimulus, and **negative** if it grows away. For example, shoots grow towards light where it is most intense (positive phototropism) and grow away from the force of gravity (negative geotropism). Roots grow to where water in the soil is most abundant (positive hydrotropism). As a result the plant is more likely to survive.

The word **behaviour** refers to the responses of animals to stimuli. **Taxes** and **kineses** are simple forms of behaviour. The terms describe the movements of animals (and other mobile organisms) that help them find environments where they are most likely to survive. Taxes (singular taxis) are directional movements which orientate an individual with respect to the stimulus causing the response.

- **Positive (+) taxis** – an individual moves towards the stimulus.
- **Negative (−) taxis** – an individual moves away from the stimulus.

Tactic responses are classified according to the type of stimulus, e.g. light – phototaxis; chemicals – chemotaxis.

Kineses (singular kinesis) are random non-directional movements: an individual does not move towards or away from a stimulus but moves faster and changes direction more frequently.

The individual's response reflects the intensity of a stimulus which threatens its survival. The more intense the threatening stimulus, the faster are the movements and the more frequent the changes of direction. Therefore the individual is more likely to find a less threatening environment. The movements then slow and may stop altogether, and so the individual spends more time in an environment where it is more likely to survive. Like taxes, kinetic responses are classified according to the type of stimulus, e.g. photokinesis.

Examples of taxes and kineses

Maggots (fly larvae) and woodlice quickly lose water from the body in dry air, threatening their survival. The air of open, brightly lit habitats is likely to be drier than the air of shaded, dimly lit habitats. Maggots and woodlice are more likely to be found in dimly lit habitats where air is **humid** (saturated with water vapour), loss of water from the body is reduced, and maggots and woodlice are more likely to survive.

How do maggots and woodlice find dimly lit habitats? Maggots are negatively phototactic; they move away from bright light. They move towards dim light and they are more likely to survive in the humid air associated with dimly lit habitats.

Woodlice are photokinetic; they move faster and change direction more frequently the brighter (more intense) the light (and therefore the drier the air). The more active woodlice are more likely to find a dimly lit habitat where the air is more likely to be humid; woodlice are much less active in dimly lit habitats, and they are more likely to remain there and survive.

Key term

A **stimulus** is a change in the environment that causes an organism to take action. The action taken is the **response**.

Summary questions

1 What is a stimulus? What is a response? (*3 marks*)

2 What is the difference between a positive tropism and a negative tropism? (*4 marks*)

3 Explain the difference between taxes and kineses. (*4 marks*)

Growth factors and plant responses

A plant's response to

- unidirectional light is called **phototropism**
- the unidirectional pull of gravity is called **gravitropism**
- where water is in the greatest amount is called **hydrotropism**.

Discovering indoleacetic acid (IAA)

In 1928, the Dutch plant biologist Frits Went investigated the response of seedlings to unidirectional light. The results of his experiments suggested that a substance is produced in the tips of shoots, passes to the region behind the tip, and stimulates growth so that the shoots grow towards unidirectional light.

The substance that Went collected was called **auxin** (from the Greek word auxein 'to grow'). In 1934, auxin was identified as **indoleacetic acid (IAA)**. It is widely distributed in plant tissues and regulates their growth. After IAA was isolated other substances regulating plant growth were discovered.

How does IAA work?

IAA stimulates cells to secrete protons (H^+), lowering the pH of the external environment of the affected cells. The increasing acidity loosens the bundling of the cellulose fibres of the cell walls. Affected cells maintain a low internal water potential. Water enters the cell by osmosis. The increase in hydrostatic pressure causes the cells to elongate, helped by the more loosely bound framework of cellulose fibres in the cell walls. If cell elongation occurs on one side of the shoot only, then the shoot curves. Curvature is due to cell elongation and to the synthesis of cell wall materials.

Phototropism, gravitropism, and auxin

IAA is synthesised in young leaves and the tips of shoots. A small amount may also be synthesised in the tips of roots. Its transport is by diffusion from cell to cell and translocation in the phloem from shoots to roots.

Elongation of cells is either stimulated or inhibited depending on the concentration of IAA and its location in plant tissues (see Figure 1). The concentration of IAA which stimulates the growth of shoots also inhibits the growth of roots (see Figure 2).

Common misconception

Substances regulating plant growth used to be called 'plant hormones'. Now they are usually called plant growth factors (regulators).

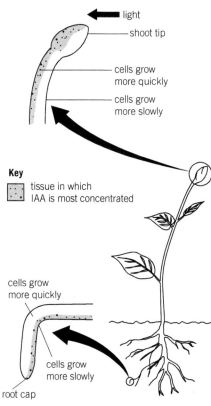

Key

▢ tissue in which IAA is most concentrated

▲ **Figure 1** *In shoots, the faster elongation of cells on the shaded side results in its curvature towards the light source. In roots, the slower elongation of cells on the lower side results in its curvature downwards*

Summary questions

1 How does IAA work?
                    (6 marks)

2 Plant growth regulators help plants survive. Explain why.   (4 marks)

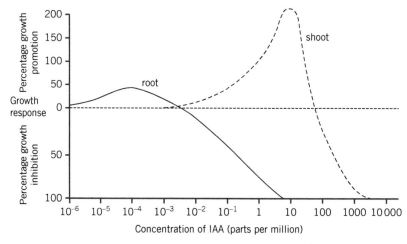

▲ **Figure 2** *IAA stimulates elongation in shoots and inhibits it in roots. These are affected by the concentration of IAA. The scale for IAA concentration is logarithmic*

14.3 A reflex arc

Specification reference: 3.6.1.1

Nerves and the nervous system

Neurones (nerve cells) are grouped into bundles called **nerves** which pass to all of the muscles and glands (the effectors) of the body. The nerves form the **nervous system**:

- the **central nervous system** consists of the brain and spinal (nerve) cord
- the **peripheral nervous system** consists of the cranial nerves and spinal nerves joining the central nervous system.

If an individual's response to a stimulus is controlled by the brain it is called a **voluntary** response. Thinking and decision are part of the process. If thinking and decision are not involved then the response is said to be **involuntary**. A **reflex response** is involuntary.

Nerves consist of bundles of hundreds/thousands of neurones. Their simplest arrangement enables an individual to respond to a stimulus. The arrangement is called a **reflex arc**. The response is a **reflex response**. We say that it is **involuntary** because it is an automatic reaction to stimuli not under conscious control. For example, we automatically jerk our hand out of harm's way if we touch a hot stove. The value to organisms of rapid reflex responses to potentially dangerous stimuli is clear. They make survival more likely.

In Figure 1, each nerve of the reflex arc is represented by only one neurone; the sensory receptor by just one receptor cell. The numbers 1–5 track the sequence of events. The process runs: stimulus → receptor → neurones → effector → response.

> **Revision tip**
> The autonomic nervous system is part of the peripheral nervous system. It controls involuntary responses, for example movement of the gut, breathing movements, and the beating of the heart.

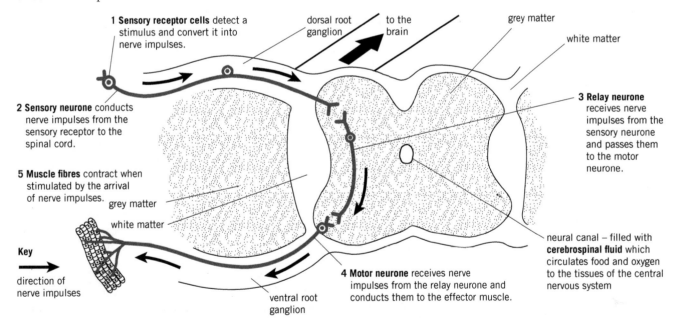

▲ **Figure 1** *Section across the spinal cord: the neurones represent the arrangement of nerves which form a reflex arc*

Summary questions

1 Explain why a reflex response is said to be involuntary. *(1 mark)*

2 Figure 2 shows a reflex arc. Explain briefly what is happening at the points labelled A–G. *(7 marks)*

3 Name the parts numbered 1–3 in Figure 2. *(3 marks)*

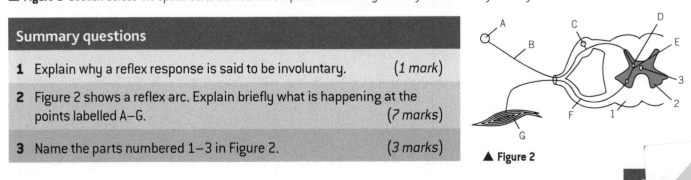

▲ **Figure 2**

14.4 Receptors

Specification reference: 3.6.1.2

Key term

Transducers: They convert one form of energy to another, for example when the cells of sensory receptors convert the stimulus into electrical energy (action potentials) to which the body can respond.

Key term

Pacinian corpuscles: Detect pressure when the skin is firmly touched.

Key terms

Sensitivity: The intensity of light required to stimulate rods and cones.

Visual acuity: The sharpness (detail) of the image we see. Remember that cones are found mostly in the middle of the retina at the fovea.

Detecting stimuli

A sensory receptor is the part of the dendrite of a sensory neurone which detects stimuli. It is the first link in the chain of events that brings about a response. Animal sensory receptors are categorised according to the stimuli they detect, e.g.

- Mechanoreceptors detect physical force such as pressure and stretch (touch, muscle contraction/relaxation).
- Photoreceptors detect light (vision).

Pacinian corpuscles

Pacinian corpuscles are mechanoreceptors. Each contains the single end of the nerve fibre of a dendrite of a sensory neurone, wrapped in layers of membrane called **lamellae**. A jelly-like material separates the layers.

The pressure of a firm touch (stimulus) deforms sodium channels in the membranes of the capsule of a Pacinian corpuscle.

- At rest, the concentration of sodium ions (Na^+) on the outer surface of the membrane of the dendrite is greater than the inner surface.
- Deformation of the sodium channels in a localised part of the membrane temporarily alters their permeability to Na^+.

As a result, Na^+ diffuses down its concentration gradient from the outer surface through the sodium channels to the inner surface of the membrane.

As a result the inner surface becomes less negatively charged. We say that the membrane is **depolarised**.

- Localised depolarisation in a Pacinian corpuscle (and other sensory receptor cells) is called a **generator potential**.
- The more intense (stronger) the stimulus, the greater is the generator potential.
- When the generator potential reaches (or is more than) a threshold value, it triggers an action potential in the sensory neurone attached to the Pacinian corpuscle.

Rods and cones

Cells called **rods** and **cones** line the retina of the human eye. The cells are photoreceptors. They convert light energy into the electrical energy of generator potentials.

Rods and cones are connected to a network of other neurones in the retina. These neurones form the fibres of the optic nerve, which pass from each eye to the visual cortex of the brain. The generator potentials formed in the rods and cones trigger action potentials in each optic nerve. The action potentials are transmitted as nerve impulses along each optic nerve to the visual cortex. Here they are interpreted as images of the object we are looking at. The connections between rods, cones, and the other neurones in the retina are shown in Figure 1.

- There are about 120 million rods in each retina. Rods are mostly found at the edges of the retina. They are only sensitive to low-intensity light.
- There are about 6 million cones in each retina.
- Cones are densely packed in the middle of the retina, particularly in the region called the **fovea**. They are only sensitive to high-intensity light.

In Figure 1, the other neurones in the retina are **bipolar neurones** and **ganglion cells**. A number of rod cells synapse with one bipolar neurone. Many bipolar neurones synapse with one ganglion cell.

The arrangement is called **convergence**.

Only one cone cell synapses with one bipolar neurone which synapses with one ganglion cell.

Overall the degree of convergence for cones is much less than rods. Usually the relationship between cones, bipolar neurones, and ganglion cells is 1:1:1.

Sensitivity and visual acuity

Sensitivity refers to the intensity of light required to stimulate rods and cones. Rods are only sensitive to low-intensity light. It is their sensitivity that enables us to see when light is dim. Convergence increases sensitivity.

- A number of rods synapse with a single bipolar neurone and many bipolar neurones synapse with one ganglion cell.

- The generator potentials from the rods are 'pooled' and generate action potentials in the ganglion cell connected to the bipolar neurones.

- Nerve impulses are transmitted along each optic nerve to the visual cortex of the brain.

- As a result, we 'see' in dim light.

- The 'pooling' of generator potentials is an example of **summation**.

- Without summation, the generator potentials of a single rod would not be sufficient to trigger action potentials in a ganglion cell.

- As a result, we would not 'see' in dim light.

- Rods are found mostly at the edges of the retina.

- As a result, seeing in dim light is best at the edges of the field of vision.

Visual acuity refers to the sharpness (detail) of the image we see. If we see closely placed points as ••• then we say that the cells of the retina have **resolved** the points as separate images. Our acuity is greater than if we see the points as •••. The points are not resolved.

- Convergence reduces acuity.

- As a result, rods do not give such high resolution as cones.

Cones are *only* sensitive to high-intensity light. The 1:1:1 relationship means that:

- each part of an image is detected by a separate cell.

- there is no 'pooling' of generator potentials.

- As a result, detail is not lost.

- Because the information of the generator potentials (and therefore the nerve impulses transmitted along each optic nerve) is not combined.

- As a result, the details of an image are resolved and the image is sharp.

- Cones are found mostly in the middle of the retina at the fovea.

- As a result, seeing in bright light is best at the centre of the field of vision (looking at objects straight ahead).

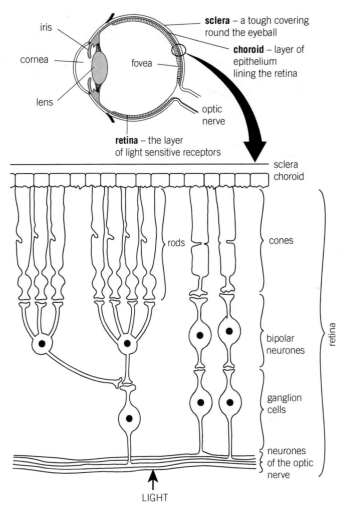

▲ **Figure 1** *Section of the retina showing the different types of cell*

Summary questions

1 Why are sensory receptors biological transducers? (*2 marks*)

2 How does a firm touch trigger an action potential in the sensory neurone attached to a Pacinian corpuscle? (*3 marks*)

3 With reference to the rods and cones of the retina of the eye, briefly summarise the meaning of sensitivity and visual acuity. (*4 marks*)

Controlling heart rate

The **heart rate** is measured as the number of ventricular contractions per minute. Usually we think of the contractions as the heart beat.

Tissue called the **sinoatrial node (SAN)** is located within the wall of the right atrium of the heart. Part of the SAN, called the **pacemaker**, determines a spontaneous average heart rate of about 100 beats per minute. The average heart rate of a healthy person at rest is about 72 beats per minute. Nervous and hormonal control of the heart rate accounts for the difference in the figures.

Figure 1 represents connections between the brain, different receptors, and the SAN. Together, they help to control the heart rate.

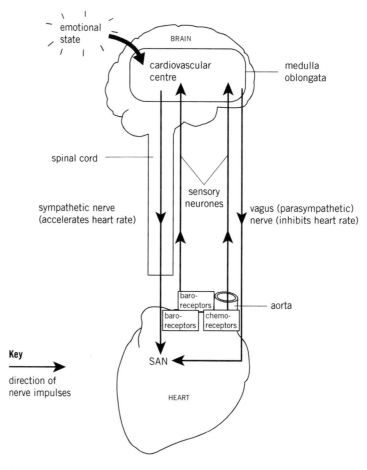

▲ **Figure 1** *Baroreceptors are a type of mechanoreceptor. They detect changes in blood pressure. The chemoreceptors detect changes in blood pH*

Revision tip
Sensory information passes from the sensory receptors to the cardiovascular centre of the medulla. Here the information is processed stimulating the sympathetic nerve and the vagus nerve. These nerves pass from the medulla oblongata to the pacemaker in the SAN.

- The **cardiovascular centre** is located in the part of the brain called the **medulla oblongata**.
- The **sympathetic nerve** and **vagus nerve** lead from the cardiovascular centre to the pacemaker in the SAN. The nerves are part of the **autonomic nervous system**.
- The sympathetic nerve passes from the cardiovascular centre to the pacemaker via the spinal cord.
- The vagus nerve is a parasympathetic nerve. It passes from the cardiovascular centre directly to the pacemaker.

- **Baroreceptors** are located in a swelling of the carotid artery called the carotid sinus, and in the walls of the heart.
- **Chemoreceptors** are located in the **carotid body**, aorta, walls of the heart, and medulla oblongata of the brain.

Nervous control of heart rate

Nerve impulses are transmitted to the pacemaker by the sympathetic nerve, which accelerates heart rate, and the vagus nerve, which inhibits heart rate.

The effect of the sympathetic nerve on the pacemaker opposes the effect of the vagus nerve. We say that the effects are **antagonistic**. A person's actual heart rate depends on the balance of activity between the nerves.

Heart rate varies

Exercise affects heart rate. It leads to an increase in concentration of carbon dioxide in the blood and as a result blood pH decreases.

- The changes are detected by the chemoreceptors in the locations shown in Figure 2.
- The sensory information passes to the cardiovascular centre. As a result:
  - The sympathetic nerve is stimulated and nerve impulses pass to the pacemaker.
  - The heart rate increases.
  - The output of blood from the heart (cardiac output) increases.
  - More blood with its load of carbon dioxide passes to the lungs.
  - More carbon dioxide is exhaled.
  - The concentration of carbon dioxide in the blood decreases.
  - Stimulation of the pacemaker by nerve impulses from the sympathetic nerve decreases.
  - Heart rate returns to normal.

The heart at work

The healthy heart at rest beats on average between 60 and 80 beats per minute: this is the **heart rate**.

The volume of blood pumped from the heart each minute (**cardiac output**) depends on the heart rate and volume of blood pumped out with each beat (**stroke volume**). Heart rate, stroke volume, and cardiac output measure the heart's effectiveness and fitness.

Cardiac output = heart rate × stroke volume

A fit heart, at rest, has up to 25% more output than an unfit heart. Stroke volume is also greater and a fit heart beats more slowly. During vigorous exercise, cardiac output is as much as 50% more and this meets the increased demand for oxygen from the muscles more efficiently.

Revision tip

The spontaneous average heart rate is about 100 beats per minute. This means that the average resting heart rate of 72 beats per minute is set by the activity of the vagus nerve.

Revision tip

Hormones also affect heart rate. Adrenaline released in response to a person's emotional state (excitement, fear) increases the heart rate. Because of the consequences of its activity, adrenaline is sometimes called the 'fight or flight' hormone.

Synoptic link

See Topic 14.4, Receptors, Topic 16.2, Feedback mechanisms, and Topic 16.3, Hormones and the regulation of blood glucose concentration.

Summary questions

1 How are the sympathetic nerve and vagus nerve antagonistic to one another? (3 marks)

2 Briefly describe the role of sensory receptors in the control of the heart rate. (3 marks)

3 What is the effect of adrenaline on the heart rate? (3 marks)

IAA binds to a specific receptor molecule on cell surface membrane.

↓

Binding changes the shape of the receptor molecule.

↓

The change in shape activates hydrogen ion (H^+) pump proteins in the cell surface membrane.

↓

H^+ ions are pumped from the cytoplasm of the cells into the cell wall.

1 The flow chart shows the way IAA (indoleacetic acid) possibly affects cell walls.

a How does the mechanism reduce the pH of the cell wall? *(1 mark)*

b How does the change in pH affect the structure of the cell wall? *(1 mark)*

c Describe two similarities between this pathway and that involved in the action of the hormone adrenaline. *(2 marks)*

2 The response of woodlice to light is an example of photokinesis. It enables woodlice to find and remain in an environment that favours their survival.

Woodlice quickly lose water from the body to low-humidity (dry) air, threatening their survival.

A choice chamber can be used to investigate the responses of woodlice to light and humidity. The diagram shows you the idea.

A sample of woodlice is put into the choice chamber. A gauze separates the upper part of the chamber from the lower part that provides four different environments as shown in the diagram. This gauze floor enables the woodlice to move to environments of choice.

Use the information and your own knowledge to answer the following questions

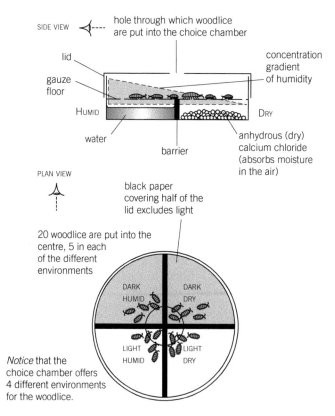

a Distinguish between phototaxis and photokinesis. *(4 marks)*

b In the diagram, the environments labelled 'dry' have granules of anhydrous calcium chloride beneath the gauze floor covering these part of the choice chamber. The other parts labelled humid contain water beneath the gauze floor. Explain how the setup makes it possible to test the response of woodlice to humidity. *(3 marks)*

c After introduction to the choice chamber, the woodlice were allowed 5 minutes to move to their preferred environment. The majority were found in the dark and humid environment. Explain these results. *(4 marks)*

15.1 Neurones and nervous coordination

Specification reference: 3.6.2.1

Coordination

An individual's coordinated responses to changes in the environment (stimuli) are the result of the coordinated activities of the nervous system and endocrine system. Although their activities may be coordinated, the two systems work in different ways.

▼ **Table 1** *Comparing the nervous and endocrine systems*

Nervous system	Endocrine system
Nerve impulses are electrical and transmitted by nerve cells called **neurones**	**Hormones** are chemicals produced by different **endocrine glands** which secrete them into the bloodstream
Muscles or glands (called **effectors**) respond to nerve impulses	Hormones are transported in the bloodstream to all parts of the body. However, each hormone only affects its particular **target tissue** because only that tissue has receptors which bind to the hormone in question
Effectors respond to nerve impulses in milliseconds	The response of a target tissue to its particular hormone is long-lasting

Neurones

Nerve impulses transmitted by **neurones (nerve cells)** carry information about stimuli (detected by **sensory receptors**) to **effectors** (muscles and glands) which respond to the stimuli.

- **Sensory neurones** ending in sensory receptor cells transmit nerve impulses to the central nervous system.
- **Relay** (or **intermediate**) **neurones** link sensory neurones with motor neurones. They are within the spinal cord and the brain.
- **Motor neurones** transmit nerve impulses from the central nervous system to effectors (muscles and glands) which respond by contracting (muscles) or secreting substances (glands).

The different neurones are arranged in a reflex arc. Figure 1 shows their structure.

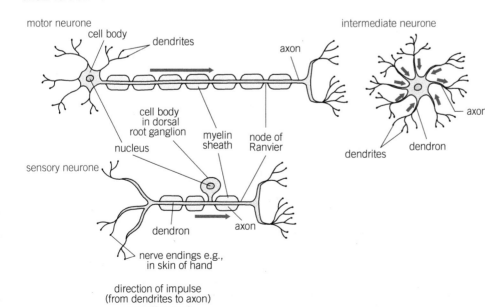

▲ **Figure 1** *Different types of human neurone*

Key terms

A **dendron** and its **dendrites**: Thin extensions of the **cell body** which carry nerve impulses towards the cell body.

Axon: An extension of the cell body that carries nerve impulses away from the cell body.

Schwann cell: A type of cell that forms the components of the myelin sheath during the development of the nervous system.

Myelin sheath: Forms from Schwann cells. It consists of layers of membrane wrapped round the axon. Myelin is a fatty substance and an important component of the sheath. It insulates the axon.

Node of Ranvier: A break in the myelin sheath where the axon is uncovered. Nerve impulses jump from node to node, speeding up their passage along the axon.

Summary questions

1 The nervous system and endocrine system work in different ways. Summarise the differences. *(6 marks)*

2 Describe the structural differences between a sensory neurone and a motor neurone. *(2 marks)*

3 Distinguish between a dendron and an axon. *(2 marks)*

Resting potential

The membrane surrounding an axon is an extension of the membrane surrounding its cell body. When open, different types of ion-channel proteins in the membrane enable sodium ions and potassium ions to pass across the axon membrane. Some of the channels are specific to sodium ions, others to potassium ions.

- More potassium ions diffuse out of the axon than sodium ions diffuse in. As a result, the inner surface of the membrane develops a negative charge relative to its outer surface (even though sodium ions and potassium ions each carry a single +ve charge). Because of this, a **potential difference** of −65 mV develops across the axon membrane. The value represents the **resting potential** of the axon membrane. We say the axon is **polarised**.

As a result, the concentration of:

- sodium ions (Na$^+$) is higher on the outer surface of the membrane than on its inner surface
- potassium ions (K$^+$) is higher on the inner surface of the membrane than on its outer surface.

Active transport maintains the resting potential.

- Sodium ions and potassium ions are actively exchanged by the **sodium–potassium pump** protein channels located in the axon membrane. For every three sodium ions removed from the axon by the sodium–potassium pump, two potassium ions are brought in.

As a result, there are more positive ions on the outer surface of the membrane than on its inner surface. The negativity of the inner surface of the axon membrane established by the outward diffusion of potassium ions is maintained and a resting potential of −65 mV is maintained.

Action potential

A stimulus causes the potential difference across the membrane of the axon of the stimulated neurone to change. The change in potential difference reverses the resting potential and is called an **action potential**. Figure 1 shows you what happens.

- The action of the sodium–potassium pump in the membrane of the axon stops.

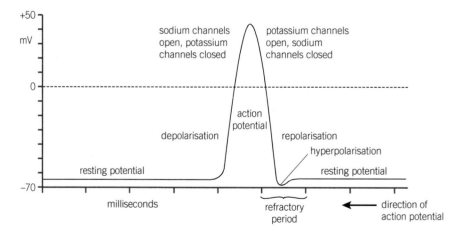

▲ **Figure 1** *An action potential: the trace shows resting and action potentials recorded by a cathode ray oscilloscope. Notice that the nerve impulse is moving from right to left*

As a result, voltage-dependent sodium ion and potassium ion channels open in the membrane and the ions diffuse along their respective concentration gradients produced when the axon was at rest.

- The sodium ion channels open more quickly than the potassium channels. Sodium ions diffuse along their electrochemical gradient from where they are in greater concentration on the outer surface of the membrane to the inner surface where they are in lower concentration.

As a result, the inner surface of the membrane becomes less negative. We say that the membrane is **depolarised**.

- Positive charge builds up on the inner surface of the membrane as sodium ions continue to diffuse into the axon.
- When the electrical potential of the inner surface of the membrane reaches +40 mV compared with the outer surface, the sodium ion channels close.

As a result, sodium ions stop diffusing into the axon.

- The voltage-dependent potassium ion channels in the membrane remain open. Potassium ions diffuse along their electrochemical gradient from where they are in greater concentration on the inner surface of the membrane to the outer surface where they are in lower concentration.

As a result, the inner surface of the membrane becomes more negative. We say that the membrane is **repolarised**.

- Voltage-dependent and voltage-independent potassium ion channels remain open even when the resting potential of −65 mV is achieved.

As a result, potassium ions continue to diffuse from the inner surface of the membrane to its outer surface. This diffusion makes the potential difference across the membrane even more negative than the resting potential of −65 mV (**hyperpolarisation**).

- Activity of the sodium–potassium pump in the axon membrane is restored.

As a result, the distribution of sodium ions and potassium ions along the outer and inner surface of the membrane is restored and the potential difference across the membrane is restored to its resting state of −65 mV.

The sodium ion channels open more quickly than the potassium ion channels which accounts for the depolarisation of the membrane when sodium ions enter the axon, and repolarisation of the membrane when potassium ions leave the axon.

Other types of potassium ion channel are voltage-independent. This explains why more potassium ions diffuse out of the axon than sodium ions diffuse in during the restoration of the resting potential.

> **Revision tip**
>
> Sodium ion channels and some types of potassium ion channel are voltage-dependent. We say they are voltage-gated because they open only when the potential difference of the membrane of the axon changes (depolarisation) following a stimulus.

Summary questions

1 Explain how the resting potential of an axon is maintained. *(3 marks)*

2 How does an axon become depolarised? *(4 marks)*

3 Explain the meaning of voltage-gated ion protein channels. *(2 marks)*

15.3 Passage of an action potential

Specification reference: 3.6.2.1

Go further

The nerves of vertebrate animals (fish, amphibian, reptiles, birds, and mammals) consist of myelinated neurones. Myelination enables vertebrates to respond quickly to stimuli. The nerves of worms, insects, snails, squids, and other invertebrate animals are unmyelinated. Their quick responses to stimuli depend on neurones each with a large diameter. These giant neurones form a system of giant nerves.

The nerve impulse

Local circuits (localised electrical currents) are generated at the leading edge of an action potential (see Figure 1). These local circuits cause depolarisation of the resting part of the membrane just ahead of the action potential.

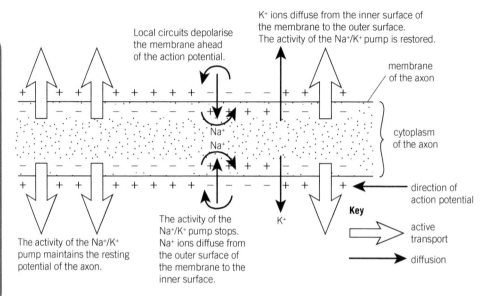

▲ **Figure 1** *The changes in the movement of ions across the membrane of the axon*

Voltage-dependent sodium channels just ahead of the action potential open.

Sodium ions diffuse down the sodium ion concentration gradient from the outer surface of the axon membrane to the inner surface and the membrane becomes depolarised.

Just behind the newly depolarised membrane the voltage-dependent sodium channels close and sodium ions stop diffusing into the axon.

Voltage-dependent potassium channels open and ions diffuse down the potassium ion concentration gradient from the inner surface of the axon membrane to the outer surface. Because of this, the part of the membrane just behind the action potential is repolarised and the sodium-potassium pump restores it to its original resting potential. As a result of successive depolarisations / repolarisations, a wave of action potentials passes (are conducted/ **transmitted**) along the axon. Transmission is the result of local circuits depolarising the membrane ahead of the action potential (see Figure 1). The conduction of an action potential is the **nerve impulse**.

Myelination and the passage of action potentials

Axons covered with myelin are said to be **myelinated**. The fatty component of myelin electrically insulates the axon. The myelin sheath of a neurone is constricted at intervals along its length. Each constriction is called a **node of Ranvier**. The myelin sheath is broken and the axon uncovered.

Depolarisation and the formation of action potentials only form at the nodes of Ranvier. Action potentials therefore jump from node to node, in a process called saltatory conduction. Action potentials pass along myelinated axons faster than along unmyelinated axons.

This is because successive depolarisations/repolarisations (action potentials) pass along the whole length of an unmyelinated axon rather than from node to node of a myelinated axon. The passage of action potentials takes more time along an unmyelinated axon than along a myelinated axon of comparable diameter.

Summary questions

1   Explain how local circuits cause depolarisation ahead of an action potential. *(2 marks)*

2   Explain why the giant axons of earthworms enable their rapid withdrawal from the attentions of a potential predator. *(3 marks)*

3   Explain how action potentials pass along a myelinated axon. *(2 marks)*

Recovery

The removal of potassium ions from the axon marks the beginning of the recovery phase. The membrane of the axon behind the action potential is repolarised and its resting potential restored. Reactivation of the sodium–potassium pump completes the process.

The period of recovery is called the **refractory period**. It lasts for about 1 ms, during which the generation of new action potentials is not possible. The refractory period determines the frequency (number per unit time) with which action potentials are transmitted along the axon, separates one action potential from another, and determines the direction of the action potentials. Action potentials cannot travel in the opposite direction because the membrane behind the action potential is refractory during the restoration of its resting potential.

Speed of conduction of action potentials

The conduction of an action potential (the passage of action potentials along the axon) is the **nerve impulse**. The speed of conduction depends on the:

- **Myelin sheath:** speeds up conduction. Action potentials only form at the nodes of Ranvier (parts of the axon not covered by the myelin sheath). Action potentials jump from node to next node in line (saltatory conduction), shortening the distance (and therefore time) action potentials are conducted along the axon. Speed of conduction reaches 120 m s⁻¹ for some myelinated axons compared with 0.5 m s⁻¹ for non-myelinated ones.
- **Diameter of the axon:** the greater it is, the less the leakage of ions and the greater is the speed of conduction.
- **Temperature:** an increase in temperature increases the rate of diffusion of ions and therefore increases the speed of conduction of nerve impulses.

Action potentials only form if the stimulus is strong enough to begin depolarisation of the membrane of the axon. The stimulus must have a **threshold** value. A sub-threshold stimulus on its own is ineffective, but a series quickly repeated may have a cumulative effect sufficient to initiate an action potential. The process is called **summation**. Once started, the amplitude of the action potential remains the same at +40 mV as it travels along an axon, regardless of the strength of the stimulus above its threshold value. In other words, the formation of an action potential is an **all-or-nothing** response.

Summary questions

1 What is hyperpolarisation?
   (3 marks)

2 Briefly explain the outcomes of the refractory period on the transmission of nerve impulses.   *(2 marks)*

3 List the factors that speed up conduction of action potentials.   *(3 marks)*

Question and model answer

Q Why is the generation of new action potentials not possible during the refractory period?

A *Hyperpolarisation at the beginning of the refractory period makes the generation of new action potentials impossible no matter how intense the stimulus.*
This is because the voltage-dependent sodium channels are closed and depolarisation cannot take place.

Hyperpolarisation and closure of sodium channels prevent generation of new action potentials.

Q Why is an action potential an all-or-nothing response regardless of the strength of a stimulus above its threshold value?

A *The depolarisation and repolarisation of the membrane of an axon depends on the concentration gradients of sodium ions and potassium ions, and the timing of the openings of the voltage-dependent ion channels.*
The concentration gradients and timings are fixed so that if a stimulus is at or above threshold value then the size of the action potential is at its maximum (all), regardless of the strength of a stimulus above its threshold value. If the stimulus is below threshold value then no action potential forms (none).

Fixed concentration gradients of ions and timings of opening and closing ion channels means that the size of the action potential is constant.

15.5 Structure and function of synapses

Specification reference: 3.6.2.2

The synapse

Figure 1 shows that the axon of a neurone ends in swellings called **synaptic knobs**. A minute gap called the **synapse** separates the knobs from the dendrites of the next neurone in line. Each knob contains numerous mitochondria and structures called **synaptic vesicles**. The membrane around a synaptic knob is called the **presynaptic** membrane. The membrane of a dendrite of the next neurone in line is called the **postsynaptic** membrane. In between each membrane is the narrow gap of the **synaptic cleft**. The gap is about 10 nm wide. Information must pass across each synapse from one neurone to the next for effectors to be able to respond to stimuli. The transmission of information across most synapses is chemical.

Figure 1 illustrates the structure of a chemical synapse. Each synaptic vesicle contains the chemical which diffuses across the synapse. The chemical is called a neurotransmitter substance, e.g. **acetylcholine**.

In Figure 1 the presence of synaptic vesicles is only in the synaptic knob. The vesicles release neurotransmitter into the synaptic cleft. The receptors to which neurotransmitter binds are only located on the postsynaptic membrane. As a result synaptic transmission occurs only in one direction: presynaptic neurone → postsynaptic neurone. The transmission of information is **unidirectional**. Information is transmitted when neurotransmitter binds to its receptors. Binding opens sodium channels in the postsynaptic membrane, which is followed by an influx of sodium ions, generating new potentials in the postsynaptic neurone called the **excitatory postsynaptic potential (EPSP)**.

Summation

On its own, an EPSP normally does not produce sufficient depolarisation to reach the threshold required to generate an action potential in the postsynaptic neurone. A number of EPSPs are required. EPSPs build up as more and more neurotransmitter substance binds to the receptors on the postsynaptic membrane. Threshold is reached when sufficient depolarisation occurs in the postsynaptic membrane to generate an action potential in the postsynaptic neurone as a whole. The additive effect of EPSPs depending on a single presynaptic neurone is called **temporal summation**.

EPSPs also build up when a number of presynaptic neurones release neurotransmitter into the synaptic cleft. The additive effect of EPSPs depending on many presynaptic neurones is called **spatial summation**. The build up of neurotransmitter opens increasing numbers of sodium channels in the postsynaptic membrane, allowing the influx of more and more sodium ions. This sequence of events leads to the generation of action potentials in the postsynaptic neurone.

Inhibition

So far the description of events refers to excitatory synapses, but other synapses work in a different way. For example, **inhibitory synapses** respond to neurotransmitter not by promoting the inflow of sodium ions into the postsynaptic neurone and the depolarisation of its postsynaptic membrane, but by promoting the outflow of potassium ions causing the polarisation of the postsynaptic membrane to increase (**hyperpolarisation**). This makes it more difficult to reach the threshold value, making the generation of an action potential in the postsynaptic neurone less likely. A postsynaptic neurone may be served by both types of synapse. Its activity is the result of the sum of their different inputs.

▲ **Figure 1** *The structure of a synapse – acetylcholine molecules bind with the receptor sites on the postsynaptic membrane because the shape of the molecules and their receptors are complementary*

> **Revision tip**
> Neurones whose synapses depend on acetylcholine are called **cholinergic neurones**.

Summary questions

1. Summarise the structure of a synapse. *(3 marks)*

2. What is the difference between an excitatory synapse and an inhibitory synapse? *(3 marks)*

3. Explain the meaning of the term temporal summation. *(2 marks)*

15.6 Transmission across a synapse

Synaptic transmission

- The arrival of an action potential at a synaptic knob opens voltage-dependent calcium channels in its presynaptic membrane, making it more permeable to calcium ions (Ca^{2+}) present in the synaptic cleft. The channels are **voltage-gated**.

- The calcium ions rapidly diffuse into the synaptic knob. They cause the synaptic vesicles filled with molecules of acetylcholine to move to the presynaptic membrane and fuse with it. The vesicles empty (an example of exocytosis) acetylcholine into the synaptic cleft (see Figure 1).

- The molecules of acetylcholine diffuse across the synaptic cleft and bind to their specific receptors on the postsynaptic membrane.

- The binding of acetylcholine molecules to their receptors opens up sodium ion channels in the postsynaptic membrane, allowing the influx of sodium ions. Depolarisation of the membrane occurs.

- The resting potential of the postsynaptic membrane is reversed and a new potential is generated.

- The new potential is called the **excitatory postsynaptic potential (EPSP)**.

After synaptic transmission

If neurotransmitter were not removed from the synaptic cleft, its presence would stimulate the repeated generation of action potentials in the postsynaptic neurone and the continuous stimulation of the effector at the end of the chain of events. If the effector is a muscle, it would be permanently contracted: a condition known as tetanus. Breaking down neurotransmitter substance prevents such an outcome.

- The enzyme **cholinesterase** located on the postsynaptic membrane catalyses the breakdown (hydrolysis) of acetylcholine into ethanoic (acetic) acid and choline.

- These products of hydrolysis pass back into the presynaptic knob.

- Hydrolysis of $ATP \rightarrow ADP + P_i$ releases energy enabling acetylcholine to be re-synthesised in the presynaptic knob from ethanoic acid and choline, and incorporated into synaptic vesicles.

- Calcium ions (Ca^{2+}) are actively transported out of the presynaptic knob, re-establishing their concentration gradient across the presynaptic membrane.

The effect of drugs on the synapse

Different drugs have their effect on the receptors of the postsynaptic membrane. Their action increases or reduces synaptic transmission.

- **Agonists** are drugs that mimic the structure of molecules of neurotransmitter substance and combine with and activate receptors. Their effect promotes the generation of action potentials. They act as stimulants.

- **Antagonists** are drugs which also mimic neurotransmitters, but when they bind to receptors they do not activate them. They block the generation of action potentials. They act as tranquillisers.

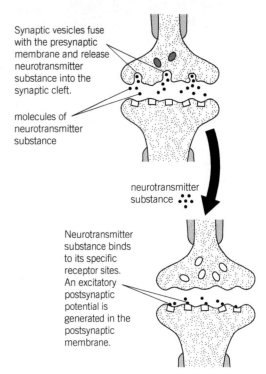

Synaptic vesicles fuse with the presynaptic membrane and release neurotransmitter substance into the synaptic cleft.

molecules of neurotransmitter substance

neurotransmitter substance

Neurotransmitter substance binds to its specific receptor sites. An excitatory postsynaptic potential is generated in the postsynaptic membrane.

▲ **Figure 1** *Transmission across an excitatory synapse*

Revision tip

The numerous mitochondria in the presynaptic knob generate the ATP required for the active transport of ions and refilling synaptic vesicles with neurotransmitter substance.

Summary questions

1 Explain the role of calcium ions in synaptic transmission. *(2 marks)*

2 The enzyme cholinesterase plays an essential role in the transmission of nerve impulses across the synapse between cholinergic neurones. Explain how. *(3 marks)*

3 Some drugs are agonists, other drugs are antagonists. What is the difference between the two types of drug? *(4 marks)*

15.7 Structure of skeletal muscle

Specification reference: 3.6.3

Key terms

The flexing effect of the biceps is opposite to the extending effect of the triceps. We say that the muscles are **antagonistic** to one another.

Muscles at work

When the muscles attached to the bones of the skeleton (skeletal muscle) contract (shorten) and relax (lengthen), the bones move at a joint (see Figure 1). The biceps and triceps are muscles attached to the upper limb bones (arm bones in humans). The contraction and relaxation enables the limb to **flex** (bend) and **extend** (straighten). The effect of each muscle is the opposite of the other. We say that muscles are **antagonistic** to one another (see Table 1).

▼ **Table 1** Antagonistic muscles

Biceps	Triceps	Position of upper limb bone (human arm)
contracted	relaxed	flexion (bent)
relaxed	contracted	extension (straight)

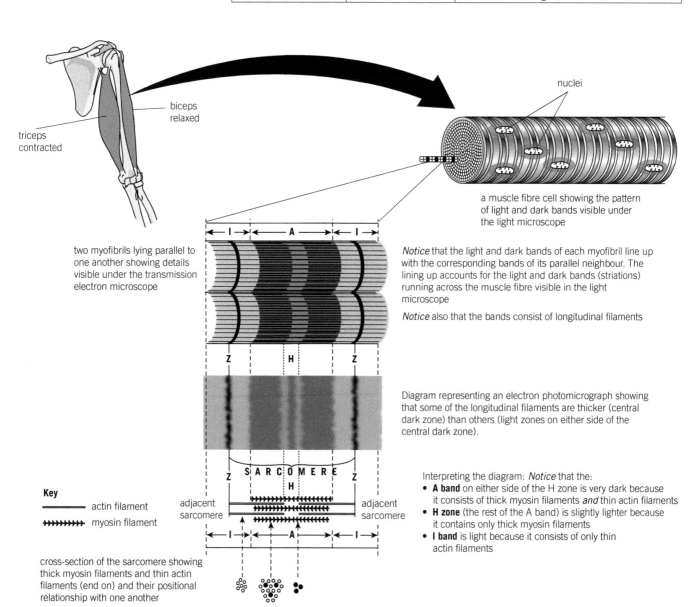

two myofibrils lying parallel to one another showing details visible under the transmission electron microscope

Notice that the light and dark bands of each myofibril line up with the corresponding bands of its parallel neighbour. The lining up accounts for the light and dark bands (striations) running across the muscle fibre visible in the light microscope

Notice also that the bands consist of longitudinal filaments

nuclei

a muscle fibre cell showing the pattern of light and dark bands visible under the light microscope

Diagram representing an electron photomicrograph showing that some of the longitudinal filaments are thicker (central dark zone) than others (light zones on either side of the central dark zone).

Interpreting the diagram: *Notice* that the:
- **A band** on either side of the H zone is very dark because it consists of thick myosin filaments *and* thin actin filaments
- **H zone** (the rest of the A band) is slightly lighter because it contains only thick myosin filaments
- **I band** is light because it consists of only thin actin filaments

Key

——— actin filament

►►►►►►► myosin filament

adjacent sarcomere

adjacent sarcomere

cross-section of the sarcomere showing thick myosin filaments and thin actin filaments (end on) and their positional relationship with one another

▲ **Figure 1** *Actin filaments are anchored to a dark band called the Z-line, running through a light region called the I-band. Myosin filaments are anchored to the M-line (not labelled) running through the middle of the H-zone. The region between adjacent Z-lines is called the sarcomere, which is the functional unit of the muscle*

Looking at skeletal muscle tissue under the optical microscope shows a pattern of light and dark **striations** (bands) running from one side to another across fibre-like cells. We say that skeletal muscle is striated (see Figure 1). Slender threads running the length of each muscle fibre are also visible. The threads are called **myofibrils**.

Figure 1 also shows that in the electron microscope:

- Each myofibril is made up of alternating light and dark bands.
- The bands of myofibrils lying parallel next to one another line up – light to light, dark to dark – accounting for the striations running across each muscle fibre.
- Each myofibril consists of a number of longitudinal filaments – some thick, others thin. Thick filaments consist of the protein **myosin**; thin filaments consist of the protein **actin**.

Slow and fast skeletal muscle fibres

Vertebrate skeletal muscle consists of two types of muscle fibre: slow-twitch fibres and fast-twitch fibres. 'Twitch' refers to the contraction of a muscle fibre in response to the stimulus of a nerve impulse. Slow twitch and fast twitch is not the only difference between the types of fibres. Other differences are summarized in Table 1.

- Myoglobin is a pigment similar to haemoglobin. It stores oxygen.
- In mitochondria, the reactions of the Krebs cycle and the electron transport chain produce large amounts of ATP.

In slow-twitch fibres:

- Aerobic respiration enables slow-twitch fibres to function for long periods without fatigue.
- The rate of ATP production during aerobic respiration is relatively slow, however.

The contractions of slow-twitch fibres are not very powerful.

In fast-twitch fibres:

- Anaerobic respiration, which quickly produces ATP using stores of creatine phosphate, enables fast-twitch fibres to function for short periods to maximum effect.

The contractions of fast-twitch fibres are very powerful.

However, anaerobic respiration in muscle fibres produces lactate. Fast-twitch fibres therefore quickly fatigue as lactate accumulates even during short bursts of activity.

The proportion of slow-twitch fibres and fast-twitch fibres in muscle tissue is genetically determined. In most people the mix is about 50:50 but in trained athletes the proportions vary.

- Long-distance runners and other endurance athletes tend to have more slow-twitch fibres.
- Sprinters and other 'power' athletes tend to have more fast-twitch fibres.

The proportions of slow-twitch and fast-twitch fibres making up our skeletal muscles may affect what sports we are naturally good at.

▼ Table 1 *Comparing slow- and fast-twitch skeletal muscle fibres*

slow twitch	fast twitch
- red coloration is the result of a high content of myoglobin - respire aerobically - numerous mitochondria	- white coloration is the result of a low content of myoglobin - respire anaerobically - few mitochondria

Revision tip

The breakdown of creatine phosphate releases phosphate ions and energy. The phosphate ions may combine with ADP, making ATP:

$$ADP + P_i \rightarrow ATP$$

Creatine phosphate is regenerated during aerobic respiration.

Summary questions

1 What are myofibrils?
(3 marks)

2 Draw a labelled diagram that identifies the pattern of light and dark bands of myofibrils. *(2 marks)*

3 What is a sarcomere?
(3 marks)

15.8 Contraction of skeletal muscle

Specification reference: 3.6.3

Revision tip
Knowing about troponin will help you to understand the role of Ca^{2+} in muscle contraction. You do not have to remember its name.

Revision tip
The term 'neuromuscular junction' refers to the synapse between a motor neurone and a muscle fibre cell.

Sliding filaments

A **myofibril** consists of a chain of sarcomeres. Understanding how a sarcomere contracts is the key to understanding how a myofibril contracts and, therefore, the contraction of muscle tissue as a whole.

How does muscle contract?

Microscopy shows that:

- Actin and myosin filaments remain the same length whether a sarcomere (and therefore a myofibril) is contracted or relaxed.
- The pattern of light and dark bands of a sarcomere changes during the contraction and relaxation of a muscle fibre.

Combined, the evidence strongly suggests that the filaments of actin and myosin slide past one another as the length of the sarcomere changes – long when relaxed and short when contracted

How actin and myosin filaments slide past one another

When muscle contracts, crossbridges form between filaments of actin and the heads projecting from the neighbouring myosin filament. Crossbridges do not form when muscle is relaxed.

- **Tropomyosin** is bound to actin. The protein covers myosin binding sites on actin molecules.
- **Troponin** binds to tropomyosin. The protein also binds to calcium ions (Ca^{2+}).

When a nerve impulse travelling along a motor neurone arrives at the synapse between the motor neurone and a muscle fibre cell, a wave of depolarisation passes into the muscle fibre cell.

- Ca^{2+} ions stored in the endoplasmic reticulum of the cell are released and bind to troponin, altering its tertiary structure.
- The change in shape causes tropomyosin to move away from the myosin binding site, uncovering it.

Only one actinomyosin crossbridge is described here. Millions of crossbridges pulling on millions of actin molecules slide actin filaments over their neighbouring myosin filament toward the centre of the sarcomere.

The role of ATP

ATPases are located in each myosin head to which ADP and P_i are bound when the muscle is relaxed. The enzymes catalyse the hydrolysis of $ATP \rightarrow ADP + P_i$, releasing energy.

- When an actinomyosin crossbridge forms, the $ADP + P_i$ bound to a myosin head are replaced by a molecule of ATP.
- The myosin head tilts, pulling the actin molecule over the myosin.
- Hydrolysis of $ATP \rightarrow ADP + P_i$, catalysed by ATPases, releases the energy needed to release the myosin head from the actin molecule.
- The myosin head flips back to its original position ('recocks').
- Contraction of the muscle continues as the result of a repeated cycle of forming and releasing actinomyosin crossbridges.
- Hydrolysis of $ATP \rightarrow ADP + P_i$ also releases the energy needed to actively transport Ca^{2+} into the endoplasmic reticulum of the muscle fibre cell.

Summary questions

1 Summarise the evidence that supports the sliding filament theory of muscle contraction. *(4 marks)*

2 How does a muscle fibre contract? *(3 marks)*

3 Explain why actinomyosin crossbridges do not form when skeletal muscle is relaxed. *(3 marks)*

1 The graph shows the changes in the permeability of an axon to sodium ions (Na^+) and to potassium ions (K^+) during an action potential. Explain how the events shown in the graph:

   a Lead to the inside of the axon becoming positive with respect to the outside during the first stage of an action potential.   (*4 marks*)

   b Restore the resting potential.   (*5 marks*)

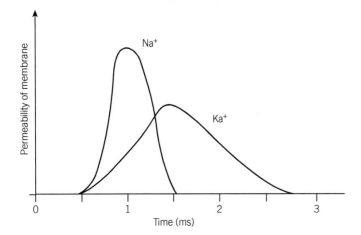

2 The Japanese puffer fish produces a substance called tetrodotoxin (TTX) which prevents voltage-gated sodium ion (Na^+) channels from opening. TTX does not affect voltage-gated potassium ion (K^+) channels. Another substance called tetraethylammonia (TEA) has the opposite effect. It prevents voltage-gated K^+ channels from opening but does not affect voltage-gated Na^+ channels.

   a Explain how treating neurones with TTX would affect their generation of action potentials.   (*2 marks*)

   b Explain why the action potentials of neurones treated with TEA last longer.   (*2 marks*)

   c Action potentials generated by neurones treated with TEA do not have a period of hyperpolarisation. Explain why.   (*2 marks*)

16.1 Principles of homeostasis

Specification reference: 3.6.4.1

Homeostasis

An organism's external environment is its habitat. Its internal environment is the tissue fluid which bathes the cells of its body, and the blood which circulates through its blood vessels. Keeping internal conditions constant is called **homeostasis**. Conditions kept constant include:

- blood glucose concentration
- blood pH (acidity/alkalinity) and water potential
- core body temperature.

The term 'metabolism' refers to all of the chemical reactions taking place in cells. Optimum temperature and optimum pH refer to the respective values at which enzymes are most active and the rates of enzyme-catalysed reactions are therefore at a maximum. Keeping blood glucose concentration, pH, and water potential constant at optimum values means that the metabolism of cells is at its most efficient.

As a result, the organism functions efficiently independent of changes (within wide limits) in its external environment and the organism's chances of survival are improved. For example, mammals and birds have a range of adaptations which enable them to live in extreme environments: polar bears and penguins survive sub-zero polar conditions; camels survive the blistering heat of deserts.

Key term

Feedback: A situation where the information about changes in the system affects what happens to the changes in the future.

Revision tip

Fat is a poor conductor of heat. A thick layer of fat (adipose tissue) reduces heat loss from the body of a polar bear to the environment, and reduces heat gain from the environment to the body of a camel.

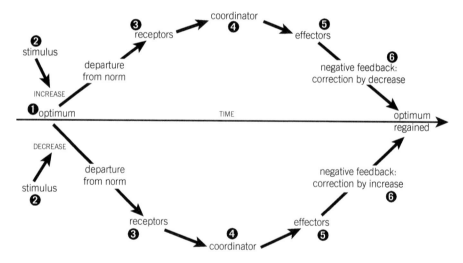

▲ **Figure 1** *Characteristics of a self-regulatory system*

Homeostasis is the result of self-regulating systems which work by means of **feedback mechanisms**. Refer to Figure 1 as you read about the characteristics of self-regulating systems:

1 **Optimum** (normal value) at which each system works. For example the blood glucose concentration of human blood is normally 90 mg glucose 100 cm⁻³ blood. Instead of optimum, the terms **set point** or **reference point** are sometimes used.

2 **Stimuli** cause deviations from the optimum.

3 **Receptors** detect deviations from the optimum.

4 **Coordinator** receives information from receptors, coordinates the information, and sends instructions to effectors.

5 **Effectors** bring about the responses needed to return the system to its optimum.

6 **Feedback** informs the receptors of the changes in the system caused by the effectors.

Summary questions

1 What is homeostasis?
(2 marks)

2 How does homeostasis enable organisms to survive in extreme environments? *(4 marks)*

3 List the characteristics of self-regulating systems.
(6 marks)

16.2 Feedback mechanisms

Specification reference: 3.6.4.1

Information and feedback

'Feedback' describes the situation where the information about changes in the system affects what happens to the changes in the future. It is the mechanism which enables cells (tissues, organs, organisms) to self-regulate their activities. When the information affects the system so that any change from the optimum:

- reverses the direction of that change towards the optimum, then we say that the feedback is **negative**

- causes more and more change away from the optimum, then we say that the feedback is **positive.**

Synoptic link

Remind yourself of the meaning of 'optimum' by looking back at Topic 1.7, Enzyme action.

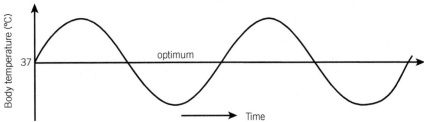

▲ **Figure 1** *Self-regulation due to negative feedback*

Negative feedback maintains stability in a system. It controls the system so that conditions fluctuate around the optimum. The system is self-adjusting. For example, human body temperature fluctuates and adjusts around 37 °C, which is the optimum temperature maximising the rate of enzyme-catalysed reactions in cells. Homeostasis depends on the negative feedback mechanisms which enable systems to self-adjust (see Figure 1).

Positive feedback does *not* maintain stability in a system. It reinforces the original change and a chain reaction quickly develops. If positive feedback runs out of control then the system may destroy itself. In the real world, however, negative feedback of some sort eventually brings the self-reinforcing changes causing the chain reaction under control. For example, damaged tissues release substances that activate fragments of cells called platelets in the blood. Activated platelets release substances which activate more platelets and so on. A chain reaction quickly develops and a blood clot forms. This breaks the chain reaction (see Figure 2), and the norm is quickly re-established (see Figure 1).

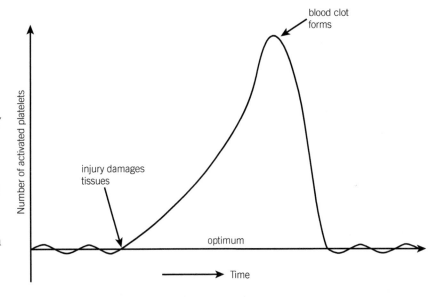

▲ **Figure 2** *Positive feedback results in a runaway chain reaction*

Substances produced during certain bacterial infections temporarily shift the core body temperature above 37 °C. The substances are called pyrogens. They affect the heat loss centre in the hypothalamus. The infected person appears flushed and produces a lot of sweat; both of these are symptoms of a fever. If homeostatic control breaks down, then positive feedback reinforces further increases in core body temperature with possible fatal results.

Revision tip

Platelets release substances in response to tissue damage. The substances stimulate platelets to stick together forming a platelet plug, because the reaction cascade that follows ends with the soluble plasma protein fibrinogen changing into insoluble fibrin. A clot forms which plugs the wound.

Summary questions

1 What is negative feedback? *(2 marks)*

2 Why does positive feedback not maintain stability in a system? *(2 marks)*

3 A pyrogen temporarily increases core body temperature above 37 °C. Explain its effects. *(2 marks)*

16.3 Hormones and the regulation of blood glucose concentration

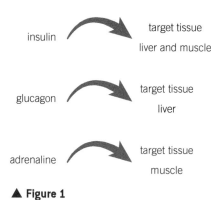

▲ **Figure 1**

Summary questions

1 What is the difference between glycogenesis, glycogenolysis, and gluconeogenesis?

(3 marks)

2 What happens when a molecule of insulin binds to its receptor protein embedded in the plasma membrane of a liver cell?

(5 marks)

3 Why is cyclic AMP (cAMP) called a second messenger molecule? What does cAMP do?

(4 marks)

The role of insulin and glucagon

Glycogen is a store of glucose in liver and muscle tissue. Different enzymes catalyse its synthesis: glucose → glycogen; and its breakdown: glycogen → glucose. The hormones insulin, glucagon, and adrenaline control the activity of the enzymes, and therefore regulate blood glucose concentration.

Messengers and receptors

The different receptors which bind molecules of insulin, glucagon, and adrenaline are embedded in the phospholipid bilayer of the plasma membrane of the cells of the hormones' target tissues (see Figure 1).

When insulin binds with its receptor:

- Endocytosis carries the hormone–receptor complex into the cytoplasm of the target cell.
- The complex stimulates the Golgi apparatus to bud off portions of material containing glucose carrier proteins.
- The material passes to the cell surface where it fuses with the plasma membrane, increasing the number of glucose carrier proteins. As a result the uptake of glucose by the cell increases.

When glucagon and adrenaline combine with their respective receptors:

- The enzyme **adenylate cyclase** is activated (adenylate cyclase is linked to the receptor protein).
- The enzyme catalyses the conversion of ATP to **cyclic AMP (cAMP)**, which is an example of a **second** messenger molecule (hormone molecules are the **first** messenger).
- cAMP activates the enzyme glycogen phosphorylase. As a result, the enzyme catalyses the breakdown glycogen → glucose. Glucose is released from the liver into the bloodstream and blood glucose concentration increases.

Glycogenesis, glycogenolysis, and gluconeogenesis

Insulin is secreted by the numerous small **beta (β) cells** of the **islets of Langerhans** of the pancreas in response to a high concentration of blood glucose (hyperglycaemia). Insulin makes the plasma membrane of liver cells and muscle cells more permeable to glucose. More glucose is taken up from the blood by the cells. It activates **glycogen synthase** (and several other enzymes), which catalyses the condensation of glucose molecules forming glycogen in liver cells and muscle cells: glucose → glycogen. The process is called **glycogenesis**. Insulin also promotes the conversion of glucose into lipids. Overall, insulin reduces blood glucose concentration.

Glucagon is secreted by the less numerous, larger **alpha (α) cells** of the islets in response to a low concentration of blood glucose (hypoglycaemia). Glucagon reduces the permeability of the plasma membrane of liver cells to glucose. Less glucose is taken up from the blood by the cells. Glucagon also inhibits glycogen synthase (and other enzymes) catalysing the reactions of glycogenesis, and activates the enzyme **glycogen phosphorylase**, which catalyses the breakdown of glycogen to glucose in liver cells. The process is called **glycogenolysis**. Glucagon also activates fructose bisphosphate phosphatase, which catalyses reactions that convert non-carbohydrate substances (e.g. glycerol, amino acids) into glucose. The process is called gluconeogenesis. Overall, glucagon increases blood glucose concentration.

Adrenaline, secreted by the adrenal glands, also affects the concentration of blood glucose. In response to a low concentration of blood glucose, it inactivates glycogen synthase and activates glycogen phosphorylase. As a result, blood glucose concentration increases.

16.4 Diabetes and its control

Specification reference: 3.6.4.2

There are two forms of diabetes. Without treatment, a person with **sugar diabetes** (a **diabetic**) may suffer from the different symptoms of hyperglycaemia:

- The pH of the blood falls, causing **acidosis**.
- The volume of water lost in the urine increases and is excessive.
- The blood supply to the body's extremities is reduced.

In the long term, **gangrene** may develop in fingers and toes deprived of the oxygen and nutrients carried in the blood.

There are two forms of diabetes:

Type 1 or insulin-deficient diabetes, where the pancreas does not produce enough insulin. The deficiency may be the result of:

- the individual's immune system destroying the β cells of the pancreas, an example of an **autoimmune disease**, or
- the gene encoding the synthesis of insulin is faulty – an example of a **genetic disorder**.

Type II or non-insulin-deficient diabetes where the pancreas produces enough insulin, at least to begin with, but the body's tissues become insensitive to it.

As a result, tissues cannot make use of blood glucose as a source of energy and the β cells of the islets produce more insulin and the liver releases more glucose.

Eventually the β cells become less able to produce enough insulin and tissues become more resistant to it.

As a result, the blood glucose concentration increases.

Treatment depends on the form of diabetes. Daily injections of insulin, together with a healthy balanced diet, regulate the blood glucose levels of individuals with Type I insulin-dependent diabetes.

Today insulin is produced using genetic engineering. The human insulin gene is inserted into *Escherichia (E.) coli*. The genetically modified (GM) bacteria produce insulin which is purified and packaged ready to treat patients with Type 1 diabetes.

Other ways of treating certain patients with Type 1 diabetes are available or are in development:

- **transplanting** the insulin-producing cells of the islets of Langerhans into patients whose diabetes does not respond to other treatments
- **immunotherapy** using a particular type of T-cell to prevent the individual's immune system destroying the islets of Langerhans.

For those with Type II diabetes, maintaining a healthy balanced diet combined with regular exercise and weight control may control the condition. However, in time, drugs that lower blood glucose levels may become necessary.

Common misconception: Causes of diabetes

The cause of diabetes is often thought to be the result of a deficiency in insulin production. However, this only applies to Type 1 diabetes. Sufficient insulin is produced, at least initially, by people with Type 2 diabetes. It is just that the target tissues for insulin in these individuals are insensitive to the hormone.

Synoptic link

Reading Topic 5.1, Defence mechanisms, Topic 5.3, T lymphocytes and cell-mediated immunity, Topic 5.4, B lymphocytes and humoral immunity, and Topic 5.5, Antibodies, will help you understand autoimmune diseases.

Summary questions

1 Which process is likely to make a gene faulty? *(1 mark)*

2 What is an autoimmune disease? *(2 marks)*

3 Explain the advantages of using genetically engineered insulin to treat Type 1 diabetes. *(3 marks)*

16.5 Control of blood water potential – structure of the nephron

Specification reference: 3.6.4.3

Kidney structure and function

Figure 1 represents a section lengthways through a human kidney and the microscopic structure of a nephron.

- The renal artery branches from the aorta. It supplies blood to the kidney. The blood contains wastes (mostly urea produced by the liver). The renal vein carries blood away from the kidney to the vena cava. The blood is clean of wastes removed by the nephrons.

- The fibrous capsule is a tough membrane round the kidney, protecting it.

- The cortex forms the outer part of the kidney. **Bowman's capsules** and the **convoluted tubules** of the nephrons are located in the cortex.

- The medulla forms the inner part of the kidney. The **loops of Henle** of the nephrons and the **collecting ducts** dip down into the medulla.

- The ureter is a tube that carries urine from each kidney to the bladder. The pelvis is the region where the ureter joins the kidney.

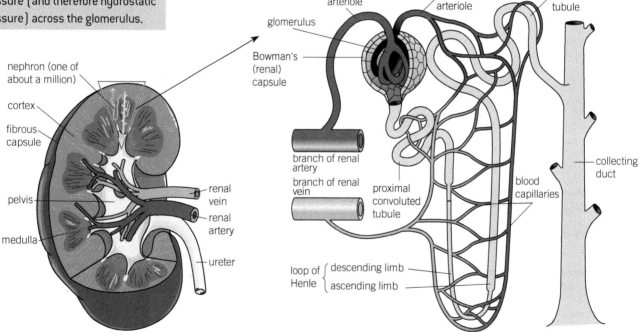

▲ **Figure 1** *Section lengthways through a kidney and microscopic structure of a nephron (not drawn to scale)*

Microscopic structure of a nephron

- The part of the nephron that filters wastes and other substances from the blood brought to it by the afferent arteriole branching from the renal artery is known as the **malpighian body**. It consists of the Bowman's capsule, a spherical hollow structure into which the substances filtered from the blood pass, and the glomerulus, a knot of blood capillaries surrounded by the Bowman's capsule and formed from the afferent arteriole. The capillary blood vessels merge to form the efferent arteriole that carries blood away from the malpighian body.

- Capillary blood vessels branch from the efferent arteriole, surrounding the convoluted tubules and loop of Henle. The vessels form the **vasa recta** and eventually drain blood to the renal vein.
- The proximal convoluted tubule is a twisted tube surrounded by the capillary blood vessels of the vasa recta. It passes to the loop of Henle.
- The loop of Henle consists of a descending limb and an ascending limb surrounded by the capillary blood vessels of the vasa recta. The ascending limb passes to the distal convoluted tubule.
- The distal convoluted tubule is another twisted tube surrounded by the capillary blood vessels.
- The collecting duct receives liquid from a number of distal convoluted tubules. Each collecting duct leads to the pelvis of the kidney where it joins the ureter.

Summary questions

1 The structures of the kidney tubule and its blood supply are listed below. Rewrite them in the order in which a molecule of urea passes from the renal artery to the outside of the body. *(5 marks)*

tubule urethra bladder glomerulus Bowman's capsule ureter collecting duct

2 The diameter of the efferent arteriole is less than the afferent arteriole. Describe the effect the difference has on the blood pressure in the glomerulus. *(3 marks)*

Specification reference: 3.6.4.3

Revision tip

The formation of urine is a two-stage process: ultrafiltration by the malpighian bodies and reabsorption by the convoluted tubules.

Revision tip

The basement membrane consists of glycoproteins and the protein collagen.

The nephron at work

Maintaining a balance between the water potential of cells and tissue fluid is important. The term 'osmoregulation' refers to maintaining the balance. Nephrons are central to the process and urine formation its outcome.

Ultrafiltration by the malpighian body

Two layers of cells sandwiching a basement membrane separate the blood in the capillary vessels of the glomerulus from the lumen of the Bowman's capsule:

- The cells forming the lining (endothelium) of the capillary are perforated by numerous **fenestrations** (pores).

- The cells forming the epithelium of the wall of the Bowman's capsule each have tiny finger-like projections with gaps between them. The cells are called **podocytes**. The basement membrane is sandwiched between the two layers of cells.

- The fenestrations of the capillary endothelium and the gaps between the podocytes allow the passage of small molecules from the blood plasma into the lumen of the Bowman's capsule.

- The basement membrane stops the passage of large molecules (most types of protein, for example) and blood cells.

- As a result the layers of cells and the basement membrane act as a filter allowing the passage of small molecules (urea) but not large molecules into the lumen of the Bowman's capsule. The process of filtration is promoted by the high blood pressure in the capillary vessels of the glomerulus. This **hydrostatic pressure** forces substances out of the blood. Other forces affect the filtration rate.

- The absence of protein in the liquid in the Bowman's capsule means that the water potential of the liquid is less negative than that of the blood in the capillaries of the glomerulus.

- As a result osmotic pressure tends to draw water back from the Bowman's capsule into the capillary blood vessels. The force is called **oncotic pressure**. It is less than the hydrostatic pressure. There is a net pressure pushing liquid from the glomerulus into the lumen of the Bowman's capsule.

Reabsorption by the proximal convoluted tubule

The cells forming the wall of the proximal convoluted tubule are ciliated and contain many mitochondria. They are metabolically active and specialised enabling:

- active transport of glucose, amino acids, and various mineral ions from the liquid in the tubule to the blood in the capillaries surrounding it

- secretion of urea into the liquid, adding to that already filtered from the blood in the glomerulus into the lumen of the Bowman's capsule

- removal of hydrogen ions (H^+) and the uptake of hydrogencarbonate (HCO_3^-), as a result of which the pH of the blood is regulated.

Reabsorption by the distal convoluted tubule

The cells forming the wall of the convoluted tubule actively transport:

- sodium ions (Na^+) from the liquid in the tubule to the blood in the capillaries surrounding it

- potassium ions (K^+), hydrogen ions (H^+), and ammonium ions (NH_4^+) into the tubule.

The rate of exchange of sodium ions and potassium ions can be varied:

- As a result, the concentration of the ions in the blood is regulated, and a blood pH of about 7.3–7.4 maintained.
- The take-up of hydrogen ions (H^+) and ammonium ions (NH_4^+) results in urine with a pH of about 6.

The proximal tubules begin the process of adjusting the levels of ions in the liquid within the tubule and in the blood. The distal tubules fine-tune the concentrations of the ions.

The loop of Henle

The liquid entering the loop of Henle from the proximal convoluted tubule is a solution of ions and other substances. As the liquid passes through the loop of Henle:

- Sodium ions (Na^+) and chloride ions (Cl^-) are actively transported from the ascending limb.
- As a result, the concentrations of sodium ions and chloride ions increase in the tissue fluid of the medulla. The water potential of the tissues of the medulla becomes more negative and sodium ions and chloride ions diffuse into the descending limb.
- Water is lost to the tissues of the medulla from the descending limb through osmosis and carried away by the blood in the vasa recta (the thick-walled ascending limb is *impermeable* to water).
- As a result, the concentrations of sodium ions and chloride ions in the descending limb increase.
- The concentrations of sodium ions and chloride ions in the loop of Henle are greatest at the bottom of the hairpin of the loop.
- As a result, sodium ions and chloride ions diffuse into the tissues of the medulla even though the concentrations of the ions in the tissues are high. The concentrations of sodium ions and chloride ions build up in the tissues of the medulla at the bottom of the loop.
- The liquid moving up the ascending limb continues to lose sodium ions and chloride ions, making it less concentrated.
- The liquid passes from the loop of Henle, through the distal convoluted tubule to the collecting ducts.

The arrangement of the loop of Henle with its descending limb and ascending limb running side by side allows the concentrations of sodium ions and chloride ions to build up at the bottom of the loop. The mechanism is called a **counter-current multiplier**.

Summary questions

1   Explain the role of the basement membrane in ultrafiltration by the malpighian body. *(3 marks)*

2   The convoluted tubules regulate the pH of the blood. Explain how. *(3 marks)*

3   Explain how the cells of the walls of the convoluted tubules are adapted to their function. *(4 marks)*

16.7 The role of hormones in osmoregulation

Specification reference: 3.6.4.3

Antidiuretic hormone (ADH)

> **Question and model answer**
>
> **Q** Why does the loss of water through osmosis from the descending limb of the loop of Henle to the tissues of the medulla not stop as the liquid flowing through the limb becomes more concentrated?
>
> **A** *The water potential of the tissues of the medulla is even more negative than the water potential of the liquid flowing through the descending limb because of the movement of ions from the loop of Henle into the medullary tissues. The water potential gradient, therefore, between the liquid in the descending limb and the medullary tissues is maintained.*

A clear understanding of water potential will help you understand the answer.

Remember the 'water potential gradient' refers to the difference in concentration of water between the regions through which water is passing by osmosis.

If the water potential of the blood is **more negative** (low) then:

- Neurosecretory cells in the hypothalamus secrete antidiuretic hormone (ADH), which passes down the axons of the neurosecretory cells to the posterior part of the pituitary gland. The hormone is released into the blood and passes to the collecting ducts.
- ADH affects the permeability of the walls of the collecting ducts to water. The more ADH, the more permeable are the walls of the collecting ducts.
- As a result of osmosis, water passes from the liquid in the collecting ducts to the tissues of the medulla along the water potential gradient maintained by the counter-current multiplier mechanism. The water passes to the blood flowing through the capillary vessels of the vasa recta.
- As a result, a small volume of urine is produced consisting of a concentrated solution of wastes and other substances.

If the water potential of the blood is **less negative** (high) then:

- The neurosecretory cells in the hypothalamus secrete and release less ADH into the blood.
- As a result, the walls of the collecting ducts are less permeable to water.
- As a result, less water passes by osmosis out of the collecting ducts into the tissues of the medulla.
- As a result, a large volume of urine is produced, consisting of a dilute solution of wastes and other substances.

Revision tip
The term *diuresis* refers to urine formation. The term *anti-diuresis* therefore refers to the prevention of the formation of urine.

Question and model answer

Q Why is the water potential of the liquid flowing into the distal convoluted tubule from the ascending limb of the loop of Henle less negative compared with blood, whereas urine leaving the collecting duct *en route* for storage in the bladder is more negative?

A *The liquid moving through the ascending limb loses ions to the tissues of the medulla. However, osmosis does not occur as the wall of the ascending limb is impermeable to water. The liquid therefore becomes increasingly dilute and its water potential is less negative compared with blood by the time it enters the distal convoluted tubule. The wall of the collecting duct however is permeable to water, which is therefore lost from the liquid flowing through it to the tissues of the medulla. The liquid becomes increasingly concentrated, and its water potential is therefore more negative compared with blood by the time it leaves the collecting duct en route through the ureter to the bladder.*

> A clear understanding of water potential is required to understand the answer.

> Remember that the water potential of pure water is zero.

> It is better to refer to water potential as being less/more negative rather than higher/lower.

The process of osmoregulation depends on monitoring the water potential of the blood by the osmoreceptors in the hypothalamus. The mechanism is another example of homeostasis controlled by negative feedback.

Revision tip
The loops of Henle of the kidney of a desert mouse are longer than the loops of Henle of the kidney of a water vole. The long loops enable a desert mouse to conserve as much water as possible, helping it to survive in the hot and dry environment. Water conservation is less important for the survival of a water vole. Its loops of Henle are therefore shorter.

Revision tip
The more deeply the loop of Henle dips down into the medulla, the greater is the build-up of sodium ions and chloride ions in the medulla and the more concentrated is the urine formed.

Summary questions

1 Explain the role of neurosecretory cells of the hypothalamus of the brain in urine formation. *(5 marks)*

2 ADH affects the permeability of the walls of the collecting ducts of nephrons to water. Explain how. *(3 marks)*

3 Protein channels called aquaporins are components of cell surface (plasma) proteins of cells of walls of the collecting ducts. The rate of absorption of water from collecting ducts into the blood is faster than can be accounted for by osmosis alone. Explain why. *(3 marks)*

1 The control of body temperature in humans is an example of homeostasis. The diagram summarises the process.

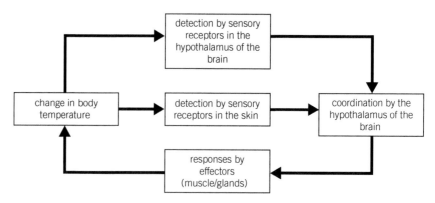

Using the diagram:

a Explain what is meant by the term 'negative feedback'. (3 marks)

b Suggest how the hypothalamus coordinates the control of body temperature. (3 marks)

2 There are two forms of diabetes: Type 1 and Type 2. Type 1 diabetes is sometimes the result of the individual's immune system destroying the beta cells of his/her pancreas: an example of an autoimmune disease.

a Which hormone is produced by the beta cells of the pancreas? (1 mark)

b An autoimmune disease is the result of an individual's immune system not recognising its own tissues. Explain what happens. (3 marks)

3 The loops of Henle of the kidney of a desert mouse are longer than the loops of Henle of the kidney of a water vole. Explain why. (4 marks)

17.1 Studying inheritance

Specification reference: 3.7.1

The meaning of important terms in genetics

Before you begin to revise genetics, you should check that you know key words and their meanings.

One characteristic passed from parents to offspring, for example flower colour or eye colour, is called **monohybrid inheritance**. **Dihybrid inheritance** refers to *two* different characteristics passing independently from parents to offspring. For example, the height of a plant and the colour of its seeds. Pure breeding refers to characteristics that breed true, appearing unchanged generation after generation.

Parental generation (symbol **P)** refers to pure-breeding individuals reproducing offspring. The offspring produced by a pure-breeding parental generation is called the **first filial generation** (symbol F_1). The offspring produced by cross-breeding members of the first filial generation are called **second filial generation (symbol F_2)**.

A **gene** is a length of DNA which encodes the whole or part of a protein. The position of a particular gene on a chromosome is called a **locus**. An **allele** is one form of a gene. The pair of alleles of a gene occupy the same locus on **homologous** chromosomes and might encode the whole or part of a protein.

A **homozygote** is an individual with a pair of identical alleles each expressing the whole or part of the same protein. A **heterozygote** is an individual with a pair of different alleles, each of which encodes the whole or part of a different protein. A gene is expressed when a protein or part of a protein is produced as a result of the transcription and translation.

Any characteristic that appears in the F_1 offspring of a cross between pure-breeding parents with contrasting characteristics, such as tallness and shortness in pea plants, or any characteristic expressed by an allele in preference to the form of the characteristic controlled by the allele's partner, or the form of the characteristic expressed by the heterozygote is said to be **dominant**. Any characteristic present in the parental generation that misses the F_1 generation but reappears in the F_2 generation, or any characteristic of an allele that is not expressed because the allele's partner is dominant, or any characteristic of an allele that is expressed only in the absence of the allele's dominant partner is said to be **recessive**. **Codominance** refers to contrasting parental alleles which are expressed equally in the phenotype of the offspring. For example, if shorthorn cattle with white coats are crossed with shorthorn cattle with red coats, the offspring have light red (roan) coats. The alleles for the antigens A and B on red blood cells are another example of codominance.

The phenomenon whereby alleles occupying different loci on the same chromosome pass together to the offspring is called **linkage**. The closer the loci the more likely linkage will occur. **Sex-linkage** refers to the alleles carried on the sex chromosomes but which do not determine the sex of offspring. For example, the allele for colour-blindness is located on the X chromosome.

A **test cross** (sometimes called a backcross) is a cross between an individual known to be homozygous recessive with an individual (of the same species) whose genotype (homozygous or heterozygous) is to be determined.

Genotype refers to the genetic make-up (all of the genes) of an individual. **Phenotype** is the outward appearance and characteristics of the cells (e.g. metabolism) of an individual which are the result of those genes of the genotype actively expressing characteristics.

A **Punnett square** is a method of setting out a cross between parents with contrasting characteristics as a table. The method was devised by the Cambridge geneticist RC Punnett (whose research papers were published between 1910 and 1958).

Summary questions

Pure-bred long-winged fruit flies (*Drosophila* sp.) are mated with pure-bred short-winged flies. The table sets out the outcomes of the matings in the F_1 and F_2 generations. Use the table to answer **Q1**, **Q2**, and **Q3**.

P	Long-winged fly × short-winged fly
F_1	All long-winged
F_2	22 long-winged flies, 7 short-winged flies

1   a   Which letter would be the most appropriate to symbolise the alleles for long-winged flies and short-winged flies? (2 marks)
    b   What are the genotypes of the two parents? (2 marks)
    c   Are the parents each homozygous or heterozygous? (1 mark)

2   a   What is the genotype of all of the F_1 flies? (1 mark)
    b   Are the F_1 flies homozygous or heterozygous? (1 mark)
    c   State the genotypes of each of the long-winged flies in the F_2 generation. Give the ratio of these genotypes. (2 marks)

3   a   What are the phenotypes of the individuals of the F_2 generation? (2 marks)
    b   What term would you use to describe the mating of one of the flies of the F_1 generation with its short-winged parent? What ratios of phenotypes would such a mating produce? (2 marks)
    c   What term would you use to describe the experiment which investigates the pattern of inheritance of a single characteristic (e.g. length of wing)? (1 mark)

17.2 Monohybrid inheritance

Specification reference: 3.7.1

Inheritance of a pair of contrasting characteristics

Genetics refers to the ways offspring inherit characteristics from their parents. Figure 1 shows how alleles controlling height of plant are inherited when homozygous tall and homozygous short pea plants are crossed.

Each cross between parents is set out as a Punnett square. The alleles of the gametes of one parent are written along the top and the alleles of the gametes of the other parent down the side. The possible combinations of alleles are written in the appropriate boxes.

T symbolises the allele that controls tall, and **t** symbolises the allele that controls short.

The contrasting characteristic, tall or short, separates in the F_2 generation in a ratio of 3:1. Other characteristics of pea plants (e.g. flower colour) also separate in the F_2 generation in a ratio of approx. 3:1.

The outcome of the cross allows us to state that:

- In general, when two pure-breeding individuals showing a pair of contrasting characteristics are crossed, the characteristics segregate (separate) in definite proportions in the second filial generation (F_2).

Or

- Of a pair of alleles, only one is present in a gamete.

T = allele controlling tall
t = allele controlling short

(a)
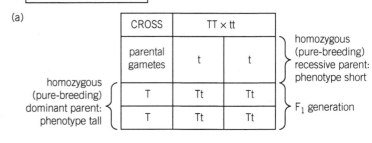

(b)
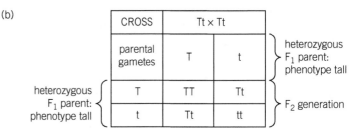

▲ **Figure 1** *Outcomes of crossing homozygous tall and short pea plants*

> **Revision tip**
> Parental alleles separate during the formation of sex cells.

Summary questions

1. The table shows the results of breeding experiments with pea plants beginning with parents pure-breeding for purple flowers and white flowers.

Cross		Original parental cross	F_1 plants from parental cross	F_2 plants from F_1 cross
Flower colour	Purple and white	All purple	770 purple: 268 white

   a Explain how you can tell from the results that the allele for purple flower is dominant and the allele for white flower is recessive. *(2 marks)*

   b To the nearest whole number, what is the ratio of purple-flowered plants to white-flowered plants in the F_2 generation? *(1 mark)*

   c All the F_1 plants are purple-flowered. Explain how the combination of their alleles is different from that of the parent purple-flowered plant. *(3 marks)*

2. What is the distinction between genes and alleles? *(3 marks)*

Summary questions

1 What do ratios represent?
    (*3 marks*)

2 Explain why the more F_2 offspring from a monohybrid cross of heterozygous parents there are, the closer the ratio will be to 3:1.   (*3 marks*)

3 The ratio of dominant to recessive phenotypes in a cross between heterozygous parents for a particular characteristic is 3:1, but the ratio of the distribution of the dominant to recessive genotypes controlling the characteristic is
    1 (homozygous):
    2 (heterozygous):
    1 (homozygous).
    Explain the link between the ratio of phenotypes and the ratio of distribution of genotypes.   (*3 marks*)

Ratios

In Topic 17.2, Monohybrid inheritance, we saw that the F_2 offspring of a monohybrid cross between two F_1 heterozygous tall parent plants segregate in the ratio of 3 tall (dominant characteristic) plants : 1 short (recessive characteristic) plant. Monohybrid crosses between F_1 heterozygous parents produce similar results. But are the results too good to be true?

Table 1 summarises results of crossing heterozygous F_1 parent plants with any one of seven characteristics.

▼ **Table 1** *Seven characteristics and the F_2 offspring*

Pairs of parental plants		Their F_2 offspring	
Dominant characteristic	Recessive characteristic	Number of F_2 plants	Dominant: recessive characteristic ratio in the F_2 sample
Green pods	Yellow pods	580	2.82:1
Axial flowers	Terminal flowers	858	3.14:1
Inflated pods	Constricted pods	1181	2.95:1
Round seeds	Wrinkled seeds	7324	2.96:1
Yellow seeds	Green seeds	8023	3.01:1

after Porteous, TW (2004) *Theoretical Biology and Medical Modelling* 1:4

- Each characteristic shows alternative dominant / recessive forms.
- F_2 phenotypes segregate nearly (but not exactly) 3 (dominant) : 1 (recessive) for any one of the characteristics.

However, you can see in the table that the larger the sample of F_2 plants examined for any one of the characteristics, the more likely the ratio of dominant to recessive phenotypes is to be closer to 3:1. Therefore, we might conclude that the larger the sample of F_2 offspring, the greater the probability that the results of a monohybrid cross between F_1 heterozygous parents will represent the predicted ratio of 3 (dominant) : 1 (recessive) F_2 phenotypes.

When plants (or any other organisms) cross, the gamete of one parent that fuses with a gamete of another parent is by chance: the fusion is random. Since 50% of the gametes of a heterozygous parent carry the dominant allele and 50% the recessive allele, and given that the fusion of gametes is random, there is the probability that 50% of the offspring will be heterozygous; the more gametes that fuse, the less likely it is that the randomness of the fusions will affect the 50:50 outcome of homozygote / heterozygote combinations of the alleles in question.

One of the alleles of the gene in question is dominant and the other allele recessive. Therefore, of the 50% homozygous combinations, half will be dominant and half recessive.

17.4 Dihybrid inheritance

Specification reference: 3.7.1

Inheritance of two pairs of contrasting characteristics

In Topic 17.2, Monohybrid inheritance, we looked at the pattern of inheritance of one pair of contrasting characteristics of pure-breeding (homozygous) tall pea plants crossed with pure-breeding (homozygous) short pea plants: a monohybrid cross. Now we look at the pattern of inheritance of two pairs of contrasting characteristics. Table 1 summarises the results of crossing pure-breeding (homozygous) tall pea plants, which produce yellow seeds, with pure-breeding (homozygous) short pea plants, which produce green seeds (a dihybrid cross).

▼ **Table 1** *Outcome of crossing two pairs of contrasting characteristics*

Cross	Original parental cross			F_1 plants from parental cross	F_2 plants from F_1 cross
Height and seed colour	Tall plants with yellow seeds	×	Short plants with green seeds	All tall plants with yellow seeds	420 tall plants with yellow seeds: 160 tall plants with green seeds: 148 short plants with yellow seeds: 46 short plants with green seeds

In Table 1 the characteristics 'height of plant' and 'colour of seed' are passed from the F_1 generation to the F_2 generation independently of one another, i.e. a tall plant and short plant may each have either yellow or green seeds. In other words the characteristics are **segregated**. The outcome of the cross allows us to state that:

- In general when two pure-breeding (homozygous) individuals showing two (or more) pairs of contrasting characteristics are crossed, the characteristics segregate (separate) independently of one another in the second filial generation (F_2).

Or

- Either one of a characteristic's alleles may be combined with either of another characteristic's alleles, the so-called law of **independent segregation**.

Table 2 sets out the results of self-crossing the tall, yellow-seeded plants of the F_1 generation. T symbolises the allele controlling tallness, t symbolises the allele controlling shortness. Y symbolises the allele controlling yellow seed, y symbolises the allele controlling green seed.

▼ **Table 2** *Dihybrid cross: genotypes and phenotypes of the F$_2$ generation. The results are displayed in a Punnett square*

Male gametes → Female gametes ↓	TY	Ty	tY	ty
TY	TYTY tall plant yellow seeds	TYTy tall plant yellow seeds	TYtY tall plant yellow seeds	TYty tall plant yellow seeds
Ty	TyTY tall plant yellow seeds	TyTy tall plant green seeds	TytY tall plant yellow seeds	Tyty tall plant green seeds
tY	tYTY tall plant yellow seeds	tYTy tall plant yellow seeds	tYtY short plant yellow seeds	tYty short plant yellow seeds
ty	tyTY tall plant yellow seeds	tyTy tall plant green seeds	tytY short plant yellow seeds	tyty short plant green seeds

The ratio of the outcomes of self-crossing the F$_1$ generation are:

tall plants with yellow seeds	9
tall plants with green seeds	3
short plants with yellow seeds	3
short plants with green seeds	1

Each characteristic has segregated independently in the F$_2$ generation and each in the proportion 3:1 dominant to recessive. Each characteristic is inherited in monohybrid fashion, but because the inheritance of two characteristics is being followed simultaneously, the ratio of the outcomes in the F$_2$ generation is 9:3:3:1, i.e. $(3:1)^2$.

Summary questions

A male fruit fly (*Drosophila* sp.) with long wings and red eyes is crossed with a female fly having short wings and white eyes. The offspring all have long wings and red eyes. One of the male offspring is then crossed with the female parent that has short wings and white eyes. The cross is a test cross. The phenotypes of the offspring of the test cross and the numbers of flies showing the characteristics are listed in the table.

Characteristics	Number of flies
long wings and red eyes	32
long wings and white eyes	28
short wings and red eyes	34
short wings and white eyes	26

1 Which letter symbols could be used to denote the alleles controlling the different phenotypes? *(4 marks)*

2 Give a brief explanation of the outcomes of the test cross. *(2 marks)*

17.5 Codominance and multiple alleles

Specification reference: 3.7.1

Codominance

In Topic 17.2, Monohybrid inheritance, we saw that a parental characteristic (height of plant) may be inherited in alternative forms (tall/short) depending on whether individuals are homozygous or heterozygous for the characteristic. In heterozygous individuals, the dominant allele (tall) is expressed in preference to the recessive allele (short).

However, sometimes a characteristic of each parent is expressed together in heterozygote offspring. For example, the coats of shorthorn cattle may be red or white, but some individuals may have a light red (roan) coat because the alleles controlling red and white are equally dominant. The alleles are **codominant**.

Figure 1 shows how codominant alleles controlling coat colour in shorthorn cattle are inherited from one generation to the next.

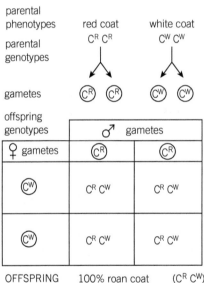

C^R = allele for controlling red pigment production
C^W = allele for controlling white (no) pigment production

F₁ OFFSPRING PHENOTYPES   100% roan coat   ($C^R C^W$)

F₁ OFFSPRING PHENOTYPES   50% roan coat   ($C^R C^W$)
25% red coat   ($C^R C^R$)
25% white coat   ($C^W C^W$)

▲ **Figure 1** *Inheritance of coat colour in shorthorn cattle*

Multiple alleles

Sometimes more than two alleles (**multiple alleles**) encode a characteristic. An individual inherits two of the alleles available. For example, the most common type of human blood group system is controlled by three alleles, A, B, and O. The A and B alleles are dominant to the O allele but not to each other (they are codominant). Table 1 sets out the possibilities. Symbols for the alleles are I^A, I^B, and I^o.

If both alleles I^A and I^B are present, then the person's blood group is AB (an example of codominance). If neither allele is present, then the person's blood group is O.

The multiple alleles for the ABO blood groups occur at different frequencies in different human populations. Table 2 sets out the different frequencies for the UK population. It seems that each blood group confers different selective advantages for the population as a whole. The genetic differences that give rise to the different human ABO groups are an example of **polymorphism**.

▼ **Table 1** *Blood groups: possible genotypes*

Genotype(s)	Phenotype: antigen on surface of red blood cells	Blood group
$I^A I^A$ $I^A I^o$	Antigen A	A
$I^B I^B$ $I^B I^o$	Antigen B	B
$I^A I^B$	Antigen A and Antigen B	AB
$I^o I^o$	nil	O

▼ **Table 2** *Frequencies of the A, B, and O blood groups for the UK*

Blood group	Percentage of UK population with blood group
A	40
B	10
AB	5
O	45

17.6 Sex-linkage
Specification reference: 3.7.1

Women are **homogametic** because their sex chromosomes are the *same* as each other. Men are **heterogametic** because their sex chromosomes are *different* from each other.

22 of the 23 pairs of human chromosomes are similar in size and shape in both men and women. These are the **autosomes**, and the alleles they carry determine the phenotype of the individual other than sex (gender). The 23rd pair are the **sex chromosomes**: **X** and **Y**. The **X** chromosome is larger than the **Y** chromosome.

- Two X chromosomes make up the sex chromosomes of a woman. Because the two sex chromosomes are the same, all her gametes (eggs) will contain an X chromosome.
- The body cells of a man carry an X chromosome and a Y chromosome. Because the two sex chromosomes are different, his gametes (sperm) will contain either an X chromosome or a Y chromosome.
- A baby's gender (sex) depends on whether the egg is fertilised by a sperm carrying an X chromosome or one carrying a Y chromosome.
- The birth of (almost) equal numbers of girls and boys is governed by the production of equal numbers of X and Y sperms at meiosis.

H = allele for production of clotting protein (rapid blood clotting)
h = allele for non-production of clotting protein (slow blood clotting)

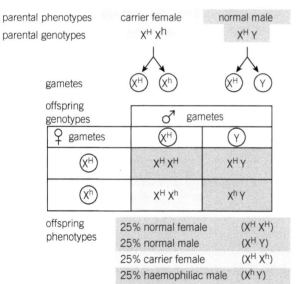

▲ **Figure 1** *Inheritance of haemophilia from a carrier female*

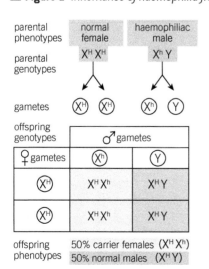

▲ **Figure 2** *Inheritance of the haemophiliac allele from a haemophiliac male*

The inheritance of gender (sex) in humans corresponds to a cross between a homozygote (the female) and a heterozygote (the male), giving a ratio of females to males of 1:1. In practice, the ratio is not quite 1:1: more males are born than females.

Haemophilia – a sex-linked disease

The X chromosome carries genes other than those which determine gender (sex). The characteristics which these genes control are said to be **sex-linked**. There is little space on the Y chromosome for genes, other than those that determine gender (sex). The fact that a female is homogametic means that she may be either homozygous or heterozygous for sex-linked characteristics. This is to her advantage if the characteristic is harmful, providing the allele controlling it is recessive. In the heterozygous state, the recessive allele is not expressed in the phenotype. The individual is said to be a **carrier** of the harmful recessive allele.

Because a male is heterogametic, he must be homozygous for any X-linked gene (the corresponding allele which might mask the effect of its X-linked partner is not carried on the Y chromosome). As a result the X-linked gene is expressed in the phenotype.

The gene responsible for the disease **haemophilia** is an example. Figure 1 shows the outcome when a woman who is a carrier of the haemophilia allele becomes a mother. One daughter is a carrier of the haemophilia allele, one son is affected by haemophilia. The other two children are not affected by haemophilia, nor is the unaffected daughter a carrier.

Figure 2 shows the outcome when a man who is a haemophiliac becomes a father. All daughters are carriers of the haemophilia alleles, and all sons are unaffected by haemophilia.

Summary questions

1 Distinguish between autosomes and sex chromosomes. *(4 marks)*

2 Red–green colour blindness is a sex-linked condition caused by a recessive allele on the X chromosome. It occurs in 8% of men but only 0.04% of women. Explain why. *(6 marks)*

17.7 Autosomal linkage

Drosophila: a model organism

The fruit fly *Drosophila* is a small fly which feeds on the sugar it finds in rotting fruit. *Drosophila* is ideal for genetic experiments.

Using *Drosophila*, the American geneticist TH Morgan found that the outcomes in the F_2 generation of dihybrid crosses between pure-breeding parents produced ratios of characteristics of 3:1 rather than the 9:3:3:1 predicted by the law of independent segregation stated in Topic 17.4, Dihybrid inheritance (see Table 1).

▼ **Table 1** *The result of crossing fruit flies, each homozygous pure-breeding for wing length and body colour*

P (pure-breeding parents)	Normal wings and grey body colour × vestigial (short) wings and black body		
F_1	All flies had normal wings and grey body colour		
F_2	Normal wings and grey body colour	:	vestigial wing and black body
	3	:	1

Morgan concluded that the genes controlling wing length and body colour had failed to segregate independently during meiosis. He also concluded that this failure was due to the fact that the genes were *located on the same chromosome* and had therefore been inherited *together* by the F_2 offspring. Genes inherited together are said to be **linked** and the term **autosomal linkage** is used, because the event involves the autosomes and not the sex chromosomes. Together, linked genes form a **linkage group**.

Figure 1 shows the outcomes in the F_2 of the inheritance of linked genes in *Drosophila* from the crosses set out in Table 1.

> **Key term**
>
> **Autosomes:** All of an organism's chromosomes other than the sex chromosomes. Autosomes are sometimes referred to as the somatic chromosomes. 'Soma' is a Greek word meaning body.

G = allele for grey body
g = allele for black body
N = allele for normal wings
n = allele for vestigial wings

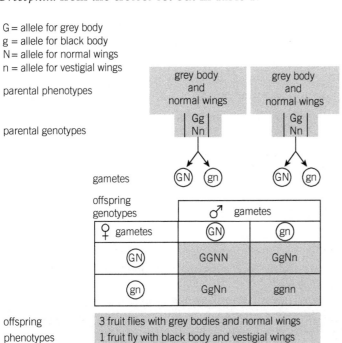

▲ **Figure 1** *The offspring of a cross between two flies that are heterozygous for both characteristics*

Morgan and his co-workers discovered four linkage groups corresponding to the four pairs of chromosomes of *Drosophila*. The equality between the number of linkage groups and the number of pairs of chromosomes is one source of evidence that genes are located on the same chromosome. Linkage groups occur in other organisms. Morgan's, and more recent, work allows two probable conclusions. If two (or more) characteristics inherited by the F_2 generation appear in the ratio of:

- 9:3:3:1, then the characteristics show independent segregation. It is probable that the alleles controlling the characteristics are not linked and are carried on *different* chromosomes.

- 3:1, then the characteristics show little if any independent segregation. It is probable that the alleles controlling the characteristics form a linkage group and are therefore carried on the *same* chromosome.

In humans, for example, the alleles controlling hair colour, skin colour, and eye colour are linked and usually inherited together: dark-skinned people usually have black hair and brown eyes; fair-skinned people often have blonde hair and blue eyes. The nearer genes are to each other on a chromosome, the closer is the linkage.

Linked genes are not always inherited together, which is why the conclusions following Morgan's work are described as *probable*. Sometimes the ratio of characteristics shown by the F_2 generation appear to conform to the law of independent segregation. In these cases, the linkage of genes has been broken by crossing over during meiosis. The linked genes separate as pieces of chromosome are interchanged. The greater the distance between linked genes on the chromosome, the more likely it is that crossing over breaks the linkage. Conversely, closely linked genes are rarely separated by crossing over. Ginger- (or red-)haired individuals are usually also freckled: the genes controlling ginger hair and freckles are closely linked.

Summary questions

Two linked pairs of alleles affecting bristle length and shape of eye in the fruit fly *Drosophila* were mapped by crossing a long-bristled fly with smooth eyes with a short-bristled fly with furrowed eyes. The F_1 flies were all long bristled and smooth eyed. When F_1 individuals were self-crossed, the numbers of individuals in the F_2 generation with combinations of different characteristics were:

Characteristic	Number in F_2 generation
long bristle, smooth eyes	275
long bristle, furrowed eyes	23
short bristle, smooth eyes	24
short bristle, furrowed eyes	78

1 State the dominant characteristics. Explain your statement. (*2 marks*)
2 Calculate the ratio of numbers of each group of individuals. (*3 marks*)

3 Which groups of individuals show a recombination of characteristics? Use your understanding of meiosis to explain why. (*3 marks*)

17.8 Epistasis

Specification reference: 3.7.1

Gene networks

Most genes do not work in isolation from one another. The majority form networks. The genes of a network interact with one another. **Epistasis** refers to the interaction where expression of the alleles of one gene masks the expression of alleles of others in a network.

A ratio of the phenotypes of the offspring of a dihybrid cross between heterozygous parents *different* from 9:3:3:1 indicates epistasis. Where a ratio of 9:3:3:1 of phenotypes of offspring is obtained from a dihybrid cross between heterozygous parents, then the outcome indicates that there is *no* epistasis.

Recessive epistasis results in a ratio of phenotypes 9:3:4 in the offspring of a dihybrid cross between heterozygous parents. Coat colour in mice is an example. There are three phenotypes: agouti, black, and albino.

Gene A: allele **A** (agouti) is dominant to allele **a** (black)

Gene B: allele **B** (colour present) is dominant to allele **b** (albino: colour absent).

Common misconception: Different forms of epistasis

Epistasis need not be only recessive. Dominant and other types of epistasis will give different F_2 ratios of phenotypes.

The outcome of crossing a homozygous agouti mouse **AABB** with a homozygous albino mouse **aabb** is F_1 offspring all heterozygous agouti: **AaBb**. The F_2 outcome of crossing within the F_1 generation is shown in Figure 1 – 9 (agouti) : 3 (black) : 4 (albino).

	♂ gametes			
♀ gametes	(AB)	(Ab)	(aB)	(ab)
(AB)	AABB	AABb	AaBB	AaBb
(Ab)	AABb	AAbb	AaBb	Aabb
(aB)	AaBB	AaBb	aaBB	aaBb
(ab)	AaBb	Aabb	aaBb	aabb

▲ **Figure 1** *Epistasis in coat colour in mice*

Gene B affects the expression of gene A. An albino mouse homozygous recessive for both genes **aabb** has the same phenotype as mice with genotypes **AAbb** or **Aabb**.

This is because the homozygous genotype **bb** is epistatic to any combination of alleles of gene A: **bb** blocks their expression, resulting in albino mice. The homozygous genotype **BB** and heterozygous **Bb** allow the expression of any combination of alleles of gene A, resulting in agouti and black mice.

Revision tip: Types of epistasis

Recessive: 2 copies of the epistatic allele are required to mask the expression of another gene, giving a ratio of phenotypes 9:3:1.

Dominant: 1 copy of the epistatic allele is required to mask the expression of another gene, giving a ratio of phenotypes 12:3:1.

Complementary: the effect of one gene combines with the effect of another gene. At least one dominant allele of each gene is required to obtain a particular phenotype. Another phenotype results from all other combinations of alleles, giving a ratio of phenotypes 9:7.

Revision tip

Coat colour is controlled by the expression (or not) of gene B producing the pigment melanin. Gene A controls its distribution.

Summary questions

1 Describe different types of epistasis other than recessive epistasis. *(4 marks)*

2 Explain why the inheritance of coat colour in mice is an example of recessive epistasis. *(7 marks)*

17.9 The chi-squared (χ^2) test

Specification reference: 3.7.1

Summary questions

1 If there are four categories of variable in a problem, how many dof are there? Explain your answer.
   (3 marks)

2 If a value of 5 dof were greater than the value given in the probability table for p = 0.05, would the results suggest a significant difference between observed and expressed results? Explain your answer. *(3 marks)*

Why the chi-squared (χ^2) test?

Many experiments generate large amounts of data. Statistical tests help us to work out what the results show.

The chi-squared (χ^2) test makes it possible to judge whether the difference between observed (O) and expected (E) values is significant. Significance is usually set at a minimum level of 95% confidence that any difference between values is real and not due to chance; we say that p = 0.05. Values of p = 0.02 and p = 0.01 mean that confidence levels are 98% and 99% respectively, which are even better! A probability table gives the critical values for a range of probabilities. If the value of χ^2 is more than the critical value for p = 0.05 then the difference between the observed (O) and expected (E) results is significant.

The chi-squared test at work

In a cross between two dark-coloured heterozygous parent flies, the offspring are expected (E) to show a 3:1 ratio of homozygous and heterozygous individuals carrying the dominant allele controlling dark colour to those homozygous individuals carrying the recessive allele controlling light colour. Table 1 sets out observed and expected results.

▼ **Table 1** *Observed numbers and expected numbers of dark coloured and light coloured flies*

Category	Observed (O)	Expected (E)
Dark	78	81
Light	30	27

Using the formula $\chi^2 = \Sigma \dfrac{(O-E)^2}{E}$

we can calculate the data to test whether the differences between observed and expected results are significant or due mainly to chance. Table 2 sets out the calculations.

▼ **Table 2** *Calculating chi-squared values*

Category	O	E	(O – E)	(O – E)^2	(O – E)^2/E
Dark	78	81	−3	9	0.11
Light	30	27	3	9	0.33

$\chi^2 = \Sigma$ 0.11 and 0.33 (0.11 + 0.33) = 0.44

Before we can compare the χ^2 value calculated (0.44 in the example) against a χ^2 probability table, we need to know the number of **degrees of freedom** (dof). Put simply, the term refers to the number (*n*) of categories of variables in the problem minus one. In the example, there are two categories of variable (dark/light), so *n* = 2 – 1, giving one dof.

If χ^2 = 0.44 is greater than the value for p = 0.05 (95% confidence) in the probability table with one dof, then the difference between the observed (O) and expected (E) results for dark/light variables is significant. In this example, χ^2 = 0.44 is less than the critical value for p = 0.05 in the probability table (critical value = 3.84). Therefore, the difference between the observed (O) and expected (E) results is not significant.

Chapter 17 Practice questions

1 When pink jellyfish of identical genotype reproduced sexually, the numbers and phenotypes of the offspring were 54 pink, 24 albino, and 18 purple. This outcome is the result of epistatic dihybrid inheritance.

   a State the epistatic ratio represented by the numbers of different coloured offspring. *(1 mark)*

   b What is epistasis? *(2 marks)*

   c What is dihybrid inheritance? *(2 marks)*

   d What kind of epistasis results in the ratio given in answer to part **a** of the question? *(1 mark)*

   e Let the symbols A and a, B and b represent the alleles of the genes, state controlling colour of the jellyfish in question. Using the symbols given, state the genotypes of the parents. *(2 marks)*

   f Explain how the different colours of the offspring arise from the genotype given in the answer to **d**. *(3 marks)*

2 The shell of the brow-lipped snail *Cepaea nemoralis* exists in a number of different phenotypes, varying from an unbanded yellow to a number of brown bands. The thrush is a predator of *Cepaea*. It breaks open the shell by holding the snail in its beak and hitting the shell against a stone. In an investigation with the aim to find out whether thrushes preferred unbanded or banded snails, empty shells of *Cepaea* were collected and sorted into 4 groups. The table sets out the observed results and the calculated expected results.

Group	Observed (O)	Expected (E)
Broken and banded	68	63.3
Broken and unbanded	30	34.7
Unbroken and banded	342	346.7
Unbroken and unbanded	195	190.3

Broken shells were assumed to have been predated by thrushes; unbroken shells not.

Using the formula

$$\chi^2 = \Sigma \frac{(O-E)^2}{E}$$

Where O = observed results
       E = expected results
       Σ = sum of

a Complete the table. The first line has already been done for you. *(3 marks)*

Group	(O–E)	(O–E)²	(O–E)²/E
Broken and banded	4.7	22.09	0.35
Broken and unbanded			
Unbroken and banded			
Unbroken and unbanded			

b Calculate the value of χ^2, showing your working. *(3 marks)*

An extract from a probability table for the appropriate number of degrees of freedom is shown below.

p	0.99	0.95	0.90	0.5	0.1	0.05	0.01	0.001
χ^2	0.00016	0.0039	0.016	0.46	2.71	3.84	6.63	10.83

c What does your value for χ^2 suggest about the relationship between banding in *Cepaea* and predation by the thrush? Give an explanation for your answer. *(5 marks)*

18.1 Population genetics

Specification reference: 3.7.2

Key term

Allelic frequency: The number of times an allele occurs in a gene pool.

Gene pool: The total of all the alleles of all the genes of a population.

Revision tip

'Disturbing influences' include selection, non-random mating, gene flare, small population size, genetic drift, and mutations.

One or more 'disturbing influences' always affect natural populations, so Hardy–Weinberg equilibrium is only possible in laboratory conditions.

Revision tip

The idea of genetic equilibrium under laboratory conditions is useful because it provides a standard against which change in gene frequencies in natural populations can be measured. The extent of change in gene frequencies of a population is a measure of its rate of evolution, so the extent of deviation from the Hardy–Weinberg equilibrium indicates the evolution of the species.

Summary questions

1 What is a gene pool?
(*2 marks*)

2 Under what conditions will the frequencies of alleles in a gene pool remain constant? (*2 marks*)

3 Of a population of sheep, 25% have black wool. The allele controlling white wool is dominant to the allele controlling black wool. What are the frequencies of the genotypes controlling wool colour in the population? (*3 marks*)

The **Hardy–Weinberg principle** states that the frequencies of alleles and genotypes in the gene pool of a population remain constant (in equilibrium) from generation to generation, unless disturbed by different influences.

Think of a population with a gene that has two alleles.

- **A** – the dominant allele: p represents its frequency in the population.
- **a** – the recessive allele: q represents its frequency in the population.

If we assume that all members of the population carry either of the alleles or both of them:

$$p + q = 1.0 \ (100\%) \qquad \textbf{(Equation 1)}$$

This shows the total frequency of the alleles in the population. Equation 1 can be used to calculate the frequency of each of the alleles in the population. For example, if the frequency (p) of allele **A** in the population is 0.40 (40%) then:

$q = 1 - 0.40 = 0.60$ (60%), the frequency of allele **a** in the population.

Using the Hardy–Weinberg principle

Most organisms are diploid and therefore carry the alleles of a gene in pairs. At meiosis, a proportion of gametes will carry the **A** allele (frequency p); likewise a proportion of gametes will carry the **a** allele (frequency q). On fertilisation the gametes combine at random to form new genotypes as:

$$\textbf{AA} + 2\textbf{Aa} + \textbf{aa} = 1.0 \ (100\%), \text{ which may be expressed as}$$
$$p^2 + 2pq + q^2 = 1.0 \ (100\%) \ \textbf{(Equation 2)}$$

Put in words, the Hardy–Weinberg principle states that if the frequency of one allele (**A**) is p and the frequency of the other allele (**a**) is q then:

$$p + q = 1 \ (\text{Equation 1})$$

and then the frequencies of the three possible genotypes are p^2 (AA), $2pq$ (Aa), and q^2 (aa), so that

$$p^2 + 2pq + q^2 = 1 \ (\text{Equation 2})$$

giving, therefore, the relationship between allele frequencies and genotype frequencies.

Equations 1 and 2 can be used to calculate the frequency of any allele and genotype in a population.

Revision tip

It is always best to use proportions when using the Hardy–Weinberg principle rather than percentages, e.g. $2pq = 0.32$ is better than $2pq = 32\%$.

Question and model answer

Q In some parts of Africa, the proportion of individuals homozygous for the recessive sickle allele is 4%. Assuming Hardy–Weinberg equilibrium, what proportion of the population would be expected to be heterozygous?

A *The frequency of homozygous recessives (q^2) = 0.04 (4% Hb^{s}Hb^s)*

$p + q = 1$, where $p =$ frequency of Hb^A and $q =$ frequency of Hb^s — Use Equation 2 to calculate the frequency of the three possible genotypes.

therefore $q = \sqrt{(0.04)} = 0.2$ and $p = 1 - 0.2 = 0.8$

therefore $p^2 = (0.8)^2 = 0.64$ (64% Hb^{A}Hb^A) — Use Equation 1 to calculate the frequency of the dominant allele Hb^A (p).

therefore

$2pq = 2 \times 0.8 \times 0.2 = 0.32$ (32% Hb^{A}Hb^s)

So 32 % is the proportion of the population expected to be heterozygous.

18.2 Variation in phenotype

Specification reference: 3.7.3

Variation

Some characteristics show variations spread over a range of measurements. Height is an example. All *intermediate* heights are possible between one extreme (shortness) and the other (tallness). We say that the characteristic shows **continuous variation**. Figure 1 shows that continuous data can be represented as a **distribution curve**, e.g. height varies about a mean which is typical for the species.

Other characteristics do not show intermediate forms but distinct categories. For example, most human blood groups are just one of A, B, AB, or O; pea plants are either tall or short (dwarf). We say that the characteristics show **discontinuous variation**. Figure 2 shows that discontinuous data can be represented as a bar chart.

Environmental causes of variation

Variation can arise from environmental causes. Examples are:

- **Nutrients** in the food we eat, and minerals that plants absorb in solution through the roots.
- **Drugs**, which may have a serious effect on appearance.
- **Temperature** that affects the rate of enzyme-controlled chemical reactions.
- **Physical training** that uses muscles more than normal, increasing their size and power.

Genetic causes of variation

Genetic causes of variation are the result of mutations and events during meiosis.

Reshuffling alleles

During meiosis, homologous chromosomes pair and then **segregate** (separate) into daughter cells following cytokinesis. The paired chromosomes segregate independently of each other. The process is called **independent assortment**. The sex cells (gametes) produced vary genetically, depending on the combination of chromosomes in each daughter cell. As a result of random mating and random fertilisation, parental alleles are recombined in new arrangements in the **zygote** (fertilised egg). Offspring are genetically different (vary) from each other and from their parents (except identical twins, which are genetically the same). Crossing over in a bivalent may involve each pair of chromatids. Very large numbers of recombinations of chromatids (and therefore alleles) are possible. The recombination of chromosomes (and therefore alleles) following crossing over may result in major changes in the organism's genome.

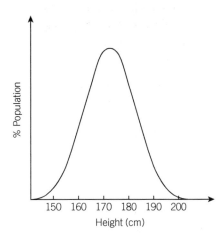

▲ **Figure 1** *The height of the majority of people falls within the range 165–180 cm*

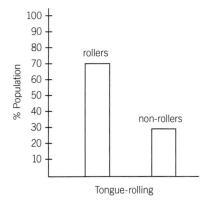

▲ **Figure 2** *Tongue-rolling – an example of discontinuous variation*

Summary questions

1. List the different ways gene mutations occur. *(3 marks)*

2. Explain the difference between a characteristic which shows continuous variation and one that shows discontinuous variation. *(2 marks)*

3. Data is often represented by its mean and standard deviation. Explain the relationship between them. *(3 marks)*

18.3 Natural selection

Specification reference: 3.7.3

Synoptic link

See Topic 18.1, Population genetics for a reminder on the meaning of a gene pool.

Key term

Carrying capacity: This refers to the resources (food, space, mates) available, enabling a population to survive in its niche.

Fundamental niche: This refers to the resources available to species in the absence of competition.

Realised niche: This refers to the resources available to species as an outcome of competition.

Revision tip

Remember that natural selection is the *mechanism* of evolution.

Revision tip

New species evolve from ancestral populations into new niches, depending on the newly evolved characteristics enabling the new species to do so.

Summary questions

1 Explain the relationship between change in an environment, competition intensity, and selection pressure. *(4 marks)*

2 Distinguish between natural selection and evolution. *(2 marks)*

3 Define the meaning of the term 'exponential'. Under what circumstances might a population increase exponentially? *(2 marks)*

Evolution through natural selection

1 Because the individuals of a species population vary genetically, their characteristics are slightly different from one another.

2 Resources (food, space, mates) enabling species populations to survive are limited.

3 Organisms have the potential to over-reproduce. However, species populations fluctuate in numbers but, on average, numbers remain stable in the medium term because the individuals of a population compete for limited resources.

4 Individuals with variants of alleles expressing characteristics that better enable the individuals to compete for finite resources in the environment in which they live (individuals are better adapted) are more likely to survive than individuals with alleles expressing less favourable characteristics (less well adapted).

5 Better-adapted individuals are more likely to survive and reproduce. Their offspring inherit the variant alleles which control those favourable characteristics.

6 The process which results in individuals being better able to compete for finite resources because they inherit variants of alleles that control the expression of favourable characteristics, promoting their survival, is called **natural selection**.

7 Competition is central to understanding natural selection:

- Organisms potentially over-reproduce.

- In theory, species populations would increase exponentially indefinitely.

- In practice, a population increases in numbers, and reaches an equilibrium corresponding to the carrying capacity of its niche.

- The realised niche sets the upper limit to the numbers of a species population.

- The observation that a species population in theory can increase exponentially, but in practice doesn't, suggests that:

  ○ The individuals of a population compete for limited resources (realised niche).

  ○ The more intense the competition, the greater the selection pressure increasing the rate of divergence of individuals of a population into races → subspecies → species (i.e. speciation: the formation of new species).

8 Alleles which control the expression of favourable characteristics accumulate in a population from one generation to the next through natural selection:

- In time, the frequency of the alleles in descendant populations is different from that in the ancestral population.

- The characteristics controlled by the alleles are therefore different in descendant populations compared with the ancestral population.

- The differences are the result of natural selection.

- Eventually populations become different species as a result of the accumulated differences between them, i.e. **speciation**.

18.4 Effects of different forms of selection on evolution

Specification reference: 3.7.3

Selection pressure

The extent of change in the frequency of an allele (or alleles) is one measure of the rate of evolution of a population. Change in an environment stimulating evolution represents **selection pressure**.

Trends in natural selection

In stable environments, selection pressure is low. For any particular characteristic (e.g. length of body), individuals with extremes of the characteristic (bodies which are short or long) are selected *against*. Those close to the average are selected *for* and are therefore more likely to reproduce (differential reproductive success), passing on the alleles controlling 'averageness' to the next generation. If the trend is long term, the species changes very little. Descendants, therefore, look like their distant ancestors. This kind of selection maintains the constancy of a species. It is called **stabilising selection.**

Where the environment is rapidly changing, selection pressure is high and new species quickly arise. Selection pressure favours those individuals with adaptations to the altering circumstances.

For example, a longer body may favour survival if predators find that catching shorter-bodied individuals is relatively easy. In these circumstances, individuals with short bodies are selected against and individuals with long bodies are selected for. Long-bodied individuals are therefore more likely to reproduce (differential reproductive success), passing on the alleles for long body to the next generation. If the trend is long term, the species changes. Descendants therefore do not look like their ancestors and may become a distinct species. This kind of selection is called **directional selection**.

Common misconception

Many think that Darwin alone came to the idea of natural selection. However, the British naturalist Alfred Russel Wallace (1823–1913) concluded that natural selection was the mechanism of evolution independently of Darwin. His letter to Darwin in 1858 setting out his (Wallace's) theory prompted Darwin to publish his book *On the Origin of Species by means of natural selection* in November 1859.

Sometimes a variety of selection pressures are at work in a particular environment. For example, a longer body may deter predators but short-bodied individuals may be able to hide from them. In these circumstances, short bodies and long bodies are selected *for*. Each type is more likely to reproduce, respectively passing on the alleles for 'long body' and 'short body' to the next generation. Average-bodied individuals are likely to be selected against because they are vulnerable to predators. If the trend is long term, then individuals of the species may co-exist in two forms (phenotypes). We say that the species is **polymorphic** for the characteristic(s). The kind of selection which favours the emergence of two forms of a species is called **disruptive selection**.

Revision tip
The lifetime's work of the British naturalist Charles Darwin (1809–1882) provided much evidence that organisms evolve. He proposed a mechanism for evolution. The mechanism is natural selection.

Key term
If a species exists in distinctly different forms (e.g. short / long body), then we say that the species is **polymorphic**.

Summary questions

1 Explain the different evolutionary outcomes of stabilising selection and directional selection.
   (4 marks)

2 Define evolution.
   (3 marks)

3 Disruptive selection gives rise to polymorphic species. Explain how.
   (2 marks)

18.5 Isolation and speciation

Specification reference: 3.7.3

Speciation

Speciation (the formation of new species) is the result of natural selection and the outcome of evolution. It occurs when isolating mechanisms lead to divergence of gene pools. What was a single population is separated into components, each called a **deme**. The individuals of each deme encounter and respond to the slightly different circumstances of the fragmented environment, so that the process of speciation gets underway. The response over time of generations of individuals of a deme is adaptation through natural selection to the slightly different circumstances.

Allopatric speciation

Earthquakes, volcanic eruptions, uplift forming mountains, and water erosion forming rivers, may bring about geographic separation that fragments a population into demes isolated from one another.

The meeting of, and matings between, individuals of the original population are interrupted and the free flow of genes is restricted to individuals of each deme.

The individuals of each deme respond to their particular environment, which may be different from the environment encountered by the individuals living in other demes. The frequency of alleles in the gene pool of each deme changes differently from the gene pool of each of the other demes, and divergence occurs as the individuals of the original population adapt within their respective deme to the environmental circumstances affecting them. Over time, new races, subspecies, and eventually new species emerge. The term **allopatric speciation** refers to this process.

Races or subspecies are extreme variants of a particular species. Their early emergence in an environment suggests fragmentation of the environment into components each with slight differences in the conditions affecting the population of the species. These differences each represent selection pressure to which each deme responds.

If then the mechanisms fragmenting the original population into demes stop having an effect, then individuals of the different races or sub species will be able to interbreed, and stabilising selection will re-establish the status quo.

If, however, the effects of the isolating mechanisms persist, then speciation will continue and new species result. If then the isolating mechanisms cease to have an effect, stabilising selection will not re-establish the status quo, as individuals of the different species will not be able to interbreed or, if they do, the offspring will probably be sterile.

Sympatric speciation

The fragmentation of a population into demes may be reproductive, in the sense that populations live in the same environment but are isolated (not exchanging alleles) from one another because individuals do not mate with one another. The free flow of alleles in the population is interrupted and divergence occurs and new species emerge. The term **sympatric speciation** refers to this process.

+ Go further: How can populations become isolated reproductively?

Ecological populations occupy different habitats within the same environment. Temporal populations live in the same area but are reproductively active at different times of the day or year. Behavioural courtship display, which is essential for successful mating, is specific for a particular species. Anatomically, the reproductive organs of the males and females of a species are usually incompatible with the reproductive organs of the males and females of another species, even if the species are closely related.

a Suggest the outcome of courtship displays that are not specific for a particular species.

b Suggest the outcome if the shape of the sex organ of the male of one species is slightly different from the shape of the sex organ of a female of a closely related species.

Summary questions

1 Give examples of circumstances which fragment a population into demes. (2 marks)

2 Explain why the process of speciation is first allopatric and then sympatric but not vice versa. (4 marks)

1 Sampling a population showed that the percentage of the homozygous recessive genotype (aa) is 36%. Use the Hardy–Weinberg functions

$p + q = 1$

$p^2 + 2pq + q^2 = 1$

where p = the frequency of the dominant allele

              q = the frequency of the recessive allele

to calculate:

a the frequency of the 'aa' genotype   *(1 mark)*

b the frequency of the 'a' allele   *(2 marks)*

c the frequency of the 'A' allele   *(2 marks)*

d the frequencies of the genotypes 'AA' and 'Aa'   *(3 marks)*

e the frequencies of the two possible phenotypes if 'A' is completely dominant over 'a'.   *(5 marks)*

In each case show your working.

19.1 Populations and ecosystems

Specification reference: 3.7.4

Living things in the environment

All of the places on Earth where there is life form the **biosphere**. Organisms are adapted (suited) to where they live. Where they live is made up of:

- an abiotic (non-living) environment of air/soil/water
- a biotic (living) community of animals, plants, fungi, and microorganisms.

An environment and its community form an **ecosystem,** which is a more or less self-contained part of the biosphere. 'Self-contained' means that the organisms living in a particular environment are characteristic of that environment because of the adaptations that enable them to live there, and not in a different ecosystem. Put simply, for example, roots anchor plants in soil; fins enable fish to swim in water.

Each type of organism (species) in an ecosystem forms a **population**. The term **ecology** refers to the relationship between populations, and between populations and the environment of the ecosystem of which they are a part. The list summarises the components of ecosystems. The organisation of the components is the same for any ecosystem.

- There is overlap where the boundaries of ecosystems meet. For example, the boundary of an oakwood is where the trees thin into grassland. Organisms from each ecosystem may be found at the boundary.
- The exchange of organisms across the boundary is limited because the organisms are **adapted** to the particular ecosystem in which they live. The unique character of each ecosystem is maintained.
- Individuals of a particular type of organism (**species**) living in a particular place at a particular time form a **population**. The **community** is made up of all of the different populations living in a particular ecosystem at a particular time.
- The **environment** is the place where a community of organisms lives.
- Different factors in the environment affect the distribution and types of organism of a community:
  - **abiotic** (physical) factors include climate, conditions of air/soil/ water, characteristics of location such as altitude (the height of land above sea level) and depth of water
  - **biotic** factors include competition, predator/prey interactions, other relationships between organisms.
- The habitat is the localised part of the environment where a population lives and which provides most of the resources its members need.
- The **niche** is the totality of all that an organism does in its habitat, including all of the resources it consumes. Resources refer to food, space, availability of mates, and other requirements which enable a species to survive in its habitat. Information about its niche tells us what a species feeds on, what feeds on it, where it rests, and how it reproduces.

Key terms

Fundamental niche: all of the resources a species can exploit in theory in the absence of competition.

Realised niche: all of the resources a species can exploit in reality because of competition.

Revision tip

In 1934 the Russian biologist G F Gause stated that a niche is occupied by only one species population at any one time. The term 'competitive exclusion' refers to the idea. No two species occupy exactly the same niche, and competition for limited resources between different species is therefore reduced.

Summary questions

1 Define ecology.	*(2 marks)*
2 What is the difference between a habitat and niche?	*(3 marks)*
3 Explain your understanding of adaptations.	*(2 marks)*

19.2 Variation in population size

Specification reference: 3.7.4

Populations

Populations are each made up of a group of individuals of a particular species living in a particular place at a particular time. **Births** and **immigration** increase the size of a population. **Deaths** and **emigration** decrease the size of a population.

Population growth

The size of a population is its number of individuals. Imagine a pioneer species colonising a new area. Provided there are no shortages of food and few predators, individuals are likely to survive and reproduce. Their numbers increase, and the population grows. The graph shows you how a population grows from small beginnings to its maximum size. Follow the sequence of numbers in Figure 1.

1 To begin with, the growth rate (number of individuals added to the population in a given time) is slow. This is called the **lag phase**.

Why? There are only a few individuals available for reproduction.

2 As the number of individuals increases, the growth rate increases. This is called the **exponential phase**.

Why? More individuals are available to reproduce. However, there is little intraspecific competition for food and the effects of disease and predators are slight.

As a result, the numbers of each generation are double the numbers of the previous generation. We say that population growth is geometric.

3 The geometric growth of a population does not continue indefinitely. As numbers build up, competition, the effects of disease and predators, and other **limiting factors** slow the rate of growth. This is called the **phase of deceleration**.

Why? Limiting factors increase the **environmental resistance** to further population growth. The effects are **density dependent** – the more individuals there are in a population, the greater is the effect of limiting factors.

4 Eventually, the rate of population growth levels off. This is called the **phase of stability**.

Why? The factors that add individuals to a population (births and immigration) are balanced by those that remove individuals from a population (deaths and emigration). The term **carrying capacity** refers to the level of resources of an environment able to sustain the maximum numbers of a population.

Abiotic factors and population size

Population growth does not always follow the pattern of a sigmoid curve. For some species, populations may rapidly increase only to 'crash'. Figure 2 shows that the growth curve is **J-shaped**.

The steep decline in numbers is usually the result of a sudden change in abiotic conditions, for example a sharp drop in temperature. The effect is **density independent** – the 'crash' occurs regardless of the size of the population and before limiting factors begin to reduce its rate of growth.

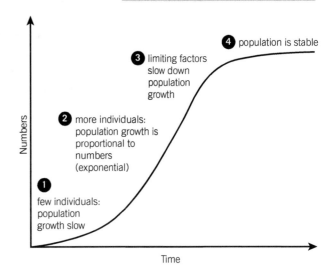

▲ **Figure 1** *Sigmoid population growth curve*

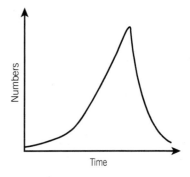

▲ **Figure 2** *J-shaped population growth curve*

19.3 Competition

In nature, living things are **competitors** (rivals) for resources which are in limited supply. The resources include water, food, light, space, and mates.

- **Intraspecific competition** refers to competition between individuals of the same species. For example, cacti are widely spaced apart. They look as if they have been planted out in a regular arrangement. Although many tiny cactus seedlings sprout in a particular area, the pattern appears because there is only enough water for some of them to grow into mature plants. Growing cacti are the competitors and water is the resource in short supply. In particular, those cacti whose root systems develop and spread the most extensively underground absorb the most water, depriving their slower-growing rivals. The extent of each root system determines the distance between neighbouring cacti.

- **Interspecific competition** refers to competition between individuals of different species. It often leads to one species displacing another from a particular niche. For example, red squirrels (*Sciurus vulgaris*) were common in woodlands throughout Britain before the introduction of grey squirrels (*S. carolinensis*) from North America in the 1870s. Now, red squirrels are restricted to a few pockets of woodland in England although they remain fairly common in Scotland. It seems that both species compete for similar types of food, but that grey squirrels are more efficient at the task. In Scotland, grey squirrels may be at the northern limits of their climate range and find it more difficult than red squirrels to survive the harsher weather.

Competition between organisms not only affects their distribution. It also has other outcomes.

Revision tip

Interspecific competition often leads to one species displacing another species from a particular niche. The displaced species either adapts to a new niche or becomes extinct.

Key terms

Interspecific competition leads to **competitive exclusion** (a species excludes another species from a particular niche). The displaced species becomes **extinct**, unless it is able to transfer and adapt to another niche.

Short-term outcomes of competition

- Intraspecific competition helps to control population size. For example, the competition by cacti for water means that slower growing plants are more likely to be affected by water shortage and therefore less likely to survive.

- Interspecific competition ensures that only one species occupies a particular niche at a particular time (the Gause hypothesis).

Available space, food, water, etc. is shared between different species, and the number of species occupying a habitat is at a maximum (biodiversity) with respect to the environmental resources available.

Long-term outcomes of competition

- Intraspecific competition is a component of **natural selection**. The individuals whose characteristics best adapt them to obtain environmental resources are more likely to reproduce (because they are more likely to survive) than less well-adapted individuals. Their offspring will inherit the alleles responsible for the favourable characteristics, and favourable alleles accumulate in the population and the species changes (**evolves**) over time.

Summary questions

1 What are abiotic factors? (*2 marks*)

2 Explain the difference between intraspecific competition and interspecific competition. (*2 marks*)

3 Explain why species may become extinct because of interspecific competition. (*3 marks*)

19.4 Predation

Interactions

'Interaction' means the way in which individuals affect each other. Interspecific interactions affect the distribution of species. Competition and the relationship between predator and prey are examples. Other forms of interaction include:

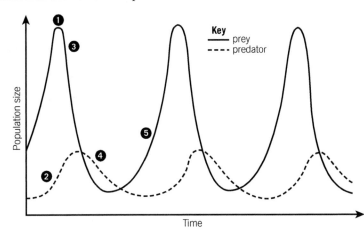
▲ **Figure 1** *How the numbers of predator and prey affect each other*

- **Mutualism** – two or more species benefit from their close relationship. Pollination in flowering plants often depends on insects. In return, the flower's visitors benefit from the sweet-tasting nectar stored in the nectaries.

- **Commensalism** – an association between one species that benefits (the commensal) and another which is unaffected either way. For example, some species of fish are immune to the sting cells on the tentacles of sea anemones. Living among the tentacles means that the fish gain protection from predators. The sea anemone seems to be unaffected by the fish.

- **Parasitism** – an association between one species that benefits (parasite) and another which is harmed (host). The parasite is usually much smaller than the host. Beef tapeworms live in the human intestines surrounded by digested food. They absorb food through the body wall. The host is deprived of food and the intestine may become blocked. The tapeworm's wastes cause illness.

Numbers of predator and prey

Predators affect the numbers of their prey. Prey has an effect on the numbers of predators. If prey is scarce then some predators starve. Figure 1 shows the relationship between the numbers of a predator and the numbers of its prey. Follow the sequence of numbers.

1. Prey breed and increase in numbers if conditions are favourable (e.g. food is abundant).
2. Predators breed and increase in numbers in response to the abundance of prey.
3. Predation pressure increases and the numbers of prey decline.
4. Predator numbers decline in response to the shortage of food.
5. Predation pressure decreases and so prey numbers increase and so on:
   - Fluctuations in predator numbers are less than fluctuations in prey numbers.
   - Fluctuations in predator numbers lag behind fluctuations in prey numbers.

There are fewer predators than prey, and predators tend to reproduce more slowly than prey.

Changes in the numbers of each population are density dependent and an example of negative feedback.

- When the numbers of prey increase, so too do the numbers of its predator, until the deaths of prey from predation exceed the number of new individuals entering the prey population through births. Then the numbers of prey decrease.

Revision tip

When numbers of prey decrease, a decrease in the number of predators follows, because of the lack of food. The effect is density dependent and an example of negative feedback.

Synoptic link

Reading Topic 16.1, Principles of homeostasis and Topic 16.2, Feedback mechanisms will remind you about homeostasis and feedback mechanisms. Refer to Topic 19.1, Populations and ecosystems for more about density dependence and carrying capacity.

Summary questions

1. List the biological outcomes of 'interactions between species'. *(3 marks)*

2. Define the phrase 'density dependent'. *(3 marks)*

3. Explain why fluctuations in numbers of a predator lag behind those of its prey. *(2 marks)*

Sampling

Populations, and the ecosystems where they live, are usually too large for it to be practical to study everything about them. Instead **samples** are taken of the ecosystem under investigation. The samples are assumed to be representative of the ecosystem as a whole. In order to study an ecosystem, the different species that live in it are quantified using two factors:

- the **distribution** – where the organisms are in the ecosystem
- the **abundance** – the number of individuals of a species relative to other species in the ecosystem.

These quantities are measured using sampling methods such as belt transects, quadrats, and point quadrats.

Fieldwork produces data that makes it possible to draw conclusions about populations and ecosystems in general. Figure 1 illustrates different ways of sampling populations in the different habitats of grassland. Using equipment which is suitable for sampling the populations is an important choice if the fieldwork is to be successful. For example, quadrats would not be useful to sample populations of fast-moving animals.

Quadrats are not suitable for sampling mobile animals. However they are suitable for sampling small static animals (e.g. limpets clinging to the rocks by the sea shore)

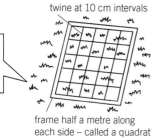

twine at 10 cm intervals

frame half a metre along each side – called a quadrat

quadrat — line of transect

positions of quadrat along transect

Quadrat – a square frame used to identify and count the number of plants or animals in a *known* area.
- throw the quadrat at random in the study area
- count the plants or animals and identify them
- calculate abundance as the number of squares that the plant or animal occupies

Reducing sampling errors
- take sufficient number of samples
- avoid choosing 'good looking' areas to sample. Remember, sampling must be *random*
- only count individual plants or animals that lie at least half inside each square of the quadrat, to estimate their abundanceaa

Belt transect – uses quadrat and line transect together. Useful for measuring changes in vegetation between two points.
- lay down tape or rope along the line of the transect
- use a quadrat to record the plant species at intervals along the transect
- estimate abundance of each species

Reducing sampling errors
- the position of the quadrat along the line of transect should follow a consistent pattern

▲ **Figure 1** *Fieldwork describes what is done to gather data from ecosystems*

An investigation is designed so that samples are taken at **random**. Random sampling means that any part of an ecosystem (its abiotic environment or populations) has an equal chance of being sampled. Different methods are used to ensure random sampling, such as a random sample generator to select samples.

Random sampling avoids bias in the data gathered during an investigation. Biased data might lead to false conclusions. We can improve confidence in data by reducing error in the sampling methods used to obtain the data.

Estimating population size

Only by counting all the individuals of a population can an absolute figure be placed on the size of a population. This approach is only possible for individuals of **sessile** (static) species which are spread out and easily seen. For motile species (individuals moving from place to place) different ways of estimating population size are used. One method is called the **capture/recapture** method or the **Lincoln index** (named after the American biologist who worked it out).

Imagine you want to find the size of a population of a species of snail. You need a small quantity of dull, water-based paint and a thin paintbrush (a twig will do).

- Dab a small spot of paint onto a known number of snails (not less than 40), returning each one to the spot where you found it.
- After a day or so, return and collect a similar number of snails. Do not specially look out for marked snails.
- Count the number of marked snails in your second collection.

The size of the snail population can be estimated using the worked example:

Question and model answer

Q A person collects a sample of 84 snails of a particular species from a small area of grass-covered bank, marks them with a dab of paint, and returns them to the place from where they were collected. A few days later, the person collects a sample of 85 snails from the same area. 42 snails of this second sample are marked with a dab of paint.

Estimate the size of the snail population.

A *Using the Lincoln index:*

$$\text{the size of the snail population} = \frac{84 \times 85}{42} = 170$$

Q Why is dull, water-soluble paint used to mark the snails?

A *Dull paint decreases the risk of marked snails being noticed by predators. Water-soluble paint eventually washes off and does not damage the snail.*

Q Why should you not specially look out for marked snails?

A *If marked snails are deliberately collected, then the size of the snail population will be underestimated.*

Summary questions

Froghoppers (small insects) live in long grass. A sample of 90 froghoppers was collected in a field using a sweep net. Each froghopper was marked with a spot of dull, water-soluble paint. A second sample taken 24 hours later produced a sample of 80 froghoppers. Six were marked.

1 Estimate the population of froghoppers in the field.   (*2 marks*)

2 Explain why dull, water-soluble paint was used to mark the froghoppers.   (*2 marks*)

3 Explain why moving a line transect would not have been a suitable method for sampling froghoppers.   (*3 marks*)

19.6 Succession

Revision tip

The flow of energy through a climax community is at a maximum.

Revision tip

People and natural events disturb environments. Clearing land for farming, fire, volcanic eruptions, and earthquakes are examples. The different successions that follow can occur on different time scales, ranging from a few days to hundreds of years.

Summary questions

1 What is the difference between a primary succession and a secondary succession?   *(4 marks)*

2 Briefly describe the relationship between flow of energy through, and productivity of, the communities of a succession from pioneer to climax.   *(3 marks)*

Communities change

Communities do not stay the same forever. They change over time as one community gives way to another. The process is called **succession**. The communities of a succession are each called a **sere**. A sere can be recognised by the collection of species that dominate at that point in a succession.

A succession begins with the colonisation of a new environment which is clear of organisms because of a **disturbance**. The colonisers are called **pioneers** and form a **pioneer community** of producers and consumers. The final sere of a succession is called the **climax community**, which is stable. Its species make-up does not change over time unless a disturbance removes them. The idea is the same for the succession in any area of land or volume of water.

- The different species of an area of land or volume of water forming a sere impact on their own environment, altering it. The changes may favour the colonisation of new species rather than the survival of the original species causing the changes. As a result, the previously dominant species may die out to be replaced by the new species.

- As the succession develops, the community of each sere is more **biodiverse** (made up of more species) than the community of the previous sere. As a result the flow of energy through the community increases from one sere to the next, the productivity of the ecosystem (area/volume) increases as the succession develops and the biomass of the community of a sere is greater than the biomass of the community of the sere preceding it.

- Succession is directional. The different seral stages in a particular succession can be predicted.

Primary and secondary succession

Succession which begins when organisms colonise an environment where previously living things were absent is called **primary succession**.

- Islands formed from volcanic eruptions (the disturbance) undersea are examples of environments where the organisms of a pioneer community establish a primary succession on the bare rock.

- Lichens are one of the few types of organism able to survive in such hostile conditions. Their activities break down the rock into particles. Their dead remains decompose, adding nutrients to the mixture, forming soil in which the species of the next sere can establish a foothold.

Succession which begins when organisms colonise an environment where previously living things were established is called a **secondary succession**.

> **Common misconception: Different types of succession**
>
> It is easy to confuse primary succession and secondary succession. Secondary succession occurs more rapidly than primary succession. On cleared land, for example, surviving seeds begin a new secondary succession.

19.7 Conservation of habitats

Specification reference: 3.7.4

Conservation: what is it?

Our well-being and ultimate survival depends on a balance between our use of resources and protecting the environments from where the resources come. Conservation enables us to achieve a balance by:

- using renewable resources (plants, animals) in a sustainable way
- reducing our use of non-renewable resources (metals, fossil fuels) through recycling and the discovery of alternative materials for the production of goods
- using land so that conflicting interests between human needs and the impact of these needs on the survival of plants and animals and their environments are reduced
- reducing pollution by the development of more efficient industrial processes, which produce less waste and use less energy
- introducing more environmentally friendly methods of farming.

Reasons for conservation

Maintaining biodiversity is central to the conservation of renewable resources. There are many reasons including:

- **Economic:** biological resources are useful to us as they provide us with food, drugs, and products such as timber, dyes, and oils.
- **Ecological:** the organisms in an ecosystem interact with each other in complex ways, and if one species is lost this can upset the natural balance and have unforeseen consequences for the rest of the ecosystem.
- **Ethical:** humans are a dominant species. Our actions can destroy habitats but our duty is to conserve them for future generations.
- **Aesthetic:** the beauty and variety of the many diverse ecosystems on Earth provide pleasure for many people.

Some communities seem to be stable and remain unchanged for long periods of time. Their stability, however, is the result of human activities. For example, we think of moorland as 'natural'. However, the moorland environment is the result of clearance of the climax community of woodland to allow grazing (the disturbance) by livestock.

In other words moorland is sub-climactic, but persists because long-term **grazing** deflects the succession from its climax. Grazing destroys seedling trees, so that the climax community of woodland cannot develop. We call moorland a **plagioclimax**.

Moorland has amenity value (we enjoy the landscape for its beauty and leisure opportunities). Our understanding of how to manage its succession through grazing by livestock long-term underpins the conservation of a highly prized environment.

A mowed lawn is another example of deflected succession resulting in a plagioclimax – providing that mowing (the disturbance) occurs regularly. However, if the lawn is left uncut, daisies and dandelions soon appear, followed by a range of other flowering plants as succession gets underway. If the lawn is left for a few years, woody plants grow up and overshadow the grass, which dies out.

Revision tip

Captive breeding by zoos is one way of conserving species close to extinction.

Summary questions

1 What is a plagioclimax?
   (2 marks)

2 Explain why maintaining biodiversity is central to conservation. *(3 marks)*

3 What are the economic benefits of maintaining biodiversity? *(3 marks)*

1 Nature reserves are set up to conserve animals and plants. The effectiveness of a reserve is often determined by its size.

Small reserves can only support small populations of animals. Explain why small reserves limit population size. *(1 mark)*

2 Three nature reserves of different size were established each carrying a different number of a particular species of monkey. The amount of genetic variation in the monkeys of each reserve was measured after one, five, and ten generations of breeding. The results are shown in the table.

Number of monkeys in each reserve at the start	Percentage (%) of genetic variation after		
	1 generation	5 generations	10 generations
2	75.0	24.0	6.0
10	95.0	77.0	60.0
100	99.5	97.5	95.0

    a Explain the differences in the % genetic variation in the monkeys of each reserve after 10 generations of breeding. *(4 marks)*

    b Explain why the results suggest that a large reserve would better ensure the conservation of the species of monkey than a small one. *(3 marks)*

3 Until the end of the 19th century red squirrels (*Sciurus vulgaris*) lived in woodlands throughout Britain. Soon after the introduction of grey squirrels (*Sciurus carolinensis*) from North America in the 1870s, the numbers and extent of territory of red squirrels declined. Grey squirrels extended their range, probably because of their greater fitness. Today red squirrels are numerous only in Scotland, and in England where grey squirrels are not established. Both species are omnivorous and particularly compete for hazel nuts (fruit containing the seeds of hazel trees) as a source of food: their niches overlap. Use the information and your own knowledge to answer the following questions.

    a From the information provided how do you know that red squirrels and grey squirrels are two different species? *(2 marks)*

    b Explain the meaning of the phrase 'greater fitness'. *(3 marks)*

    c What is a niche? *(2 marks)*

    d How do the niches of grey squirrels and red squirrels overlap? *(2 marks)*

    e The competition between grey squirrels and red squirrels is an example of interspecific competition. It not only affects their distribution but has other outcomes in the short term and long term. Identify the outcomes of interspecific competition in the

        i short term *(1 mark)*

        ii long term. *(1 mark)*

    f What is intraspecific competition? *(2 marks)*

    g What are the outcomes of intraspecific competition in the

        i short term *(1 mark)*

        ii long term? *(5 marks)*

20.1 Gene mutations

Specification reference 3.8.1

Types of mutation

Gene mutations occur when the sequence of bases is incorrectly copied during DNA replication. Nucleotides (and their bases) may be

- inserted – bases are added
- deleted – bases are lost
- duplicated – bases are repeated
- inverted – bases are turned round
- substituted – bases are copied wrongly.

Figure 1 illustrates the point.

The mutation may result in a new order in which amino acids are assembled, resulting in an error in the synthesis of protein. If only a single base pair is involved then the gene mutation is called a **point mutation** and results in base pair **deletion** (bases are lost), **addition** (bases are inserted), **translocation** (bases change position), or **substitution** (bases are replaced with others).

- The codons are set out for mRNA and are therefore complements of the DNA codons from which the mRNA is transcribed. The accepted abbreviations of the amino acid encoded by the codons are included.

- The sequence of amino acids downstream of the point mutation causing either deletion or insertion is changed compared with the normal sequence of amino acids encoded by the non-mutated gene. We say that the mutation causes a **frame shift** of bases, and frame-shift mutations can significantly affect the structure and therefore function of polypeptides.

- Substitutions also alter the sequence of bases within a codon, but not downstream of the mutation. The alteration may change the amino acid unit encoded at the point of the mutation or not. The genetic code is **degenerate**. All amino acids but two are encoded by more than one codon. This means that if the substitution replaces a base within a codon with a base of an alternative codon encoding the same amino acid, then the amino acid sequence of the polypeptide as a whole will not change, even though the base sequence of the codon has. Recall that this is why this sort of mutation is called a **silent** mutation.

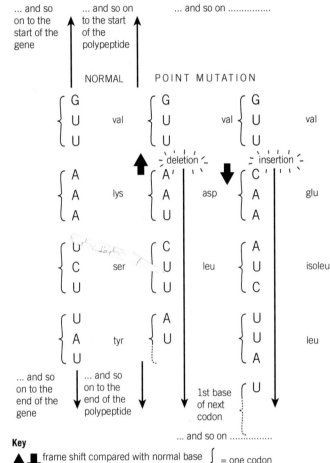

▲ **Figure 1** *Mutations have different outcomes*

Causes of mutations

Gene mutations occur spontaneously as random events during DNA replication. However various factors in the environment increase the mutation rate. An environmental factor that causes mutation is called a **mutagen**. Ionising radiation (e.g. X-rays, gamma rays) and different chemicals are mutagens.

- Ionising radiation damages DNA by stripping electrons from the atoms of its molecules (ionises the atoms).

- Alkylating agents are chemicals which transfer $-CH_3$ (methyl) and $-CH_2CH_3$ (ethyl) groups to DNA molecules, altering their activity.

Synoptic link

You can read more about mutations in Topic 9.1, Gene mutation.

Summary questions

1 List the different ways gene mutations occur. *(3 marks)*

2 How do you know the codons in Figure 1 are mRNA codons? *(1 mark)*

3 Explain the meaning of the term 'frame shift'. *(3 marks)*

20.2 Stem cells and totipotency

Specification reference: 3.8.2.1

Potent cells

The adult of a sexually reproducing organism develops from a **zygote** (a fertilised egg). During development, successive cycles of cell division by mitosis form the tissues and organs of the adult body. How is it possible that all of the different types of cell that form tissues and organs arise from a single cell (the zygote)?

Cells that give rise to all of the cell types of an organism are said to be **totipotent**. Figure 1 shows that, in mammals, only the zygote and the small cluster of cells which arise from the first few cycles of mitosis following fertilisation are totipotent. Further mitotic cycles produce a hollow ball of cells containing a mass of cells within. These cells are descendants of the totipotent cells, but different from them. They can produce most, but not all, of the cells of an organism. We say that the cells are **pluripotent**.

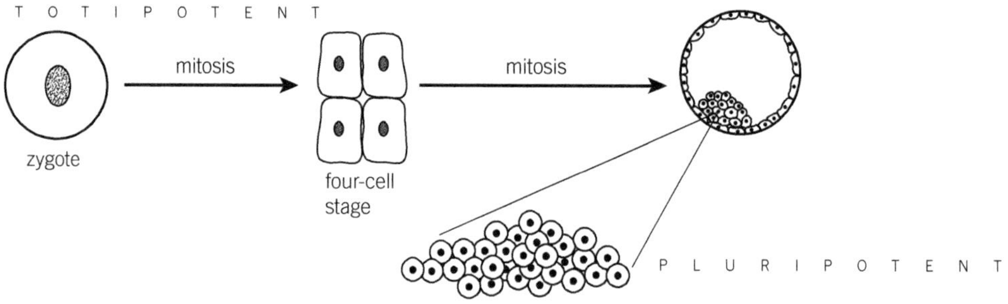

Key term

Embryonic stem cells: Derive from totipotent and pluripotent cells.

Adult stem cells: Derive from multipotent cells.

▲ Figure 1

As development of the embryo continues, multipotent cells develop. The sequence runs like this:

Stem cells are defined by their

- potential to differentiate into different cell types
- ability to divide continually by mitosis, producing new generations of cells.

The types of cell, and number of types differentiated, depend on the source of stem cell. Totipotent and pluripotent cells have the potential to differentiate into many more types of cell than multipotent cells.

Revision tip

Recently adult stem cells have been manipulated *in vitro* to produce embryonic-like stem cells. Induced pluripotent stem cells (iPS cells) can be produced from adult somatic cells using appropriate protein transcription factors. We say that the adult cells are de-differentiated.

How do cells differentiate?

During development, the differences between cells occur because only some of the genes of the pluripotent cells are expressed. Differences in gene expression (and therefore translation) result in the synthesis of different polypeptides which determine what types of cell pluripotent cells become. The process is called **differentiation**. More than 200 different types of cell make up the human body. Each type is **specialised** in ways that enable that type to carry out a particular function: for example, neurones transmit nerve impulses, muscle cells contract.

The pattern of gene expression determines the differentiation of cells and their pattern of development. It ensures that tissues and organs develop in the right place at the right time in the embryo. Getting place and time right depends on switching the transcription and translation of genes on and off in the correct order.

Summary questions

1 Explain the difference between totipotent cells, pluripotent cells, and multipotent cells.
(3 marks)

2 What is stem cell therapy?
(2 marks)

3 What is the difference between embryonic stem cells and adult stem cells?
(3 marks)

Stem cell therapy

Stimulating pluripotent stem cells to multiply and differentiate has the potential of making unlimited supplies of many different types of cell. These cells can be transplanted into people whose tissues are so damaged as to be beyond self-repair. This is called **stem cell therapy**.

20.3 Regulation of transcription and translation

Specification reference: 3.8.2.2

Regulating gene expression

Once in the bloodstream, oestrogen reaches most cells but acts only in those cells that have the type of protein receptor to which it can bind. The combination binds to a particular chromosomal protein and stimulates transcription of mRNA (see Figure 1).

1 Oestrogen is lipid soluble. It can pass easily across the phospholipid bilayer of the plasma membrane of target cells.

2 In the cytoplasm it binds to a receptor protein.

3 The oestrogen–receptor complex passes from the cytoplasm through the nuclear membrane into the nucleus where it binds to a specific chromosomal protein. mRNA transcription begins from the DNA sequence bound to that particular chromosomal protein.

4 The transcribed mRNA passes from the nucleus into the cytoplasm of the cell and binds with ribosomes.

5 The mRNA is translated into a polypeptide.

Oestrogen itself is not a transcription factor, but the oestrogen–receptor complex is. The cell's response to oestrogen is the altered function of the target cell as a result of the newly synthesised polypeptide.

siRNA regulates gene expression

Small interfering (si)RNA is one of several types of RNA molecule that help to regulate which genes are active and how active they are. Each molecule consists of short double-stranded lengths of RNA about 20 nucleotides long.

siRNA is one of the causes of **RNA interference**. The process prevents translation of mRNA and therefore 'silences' genes.

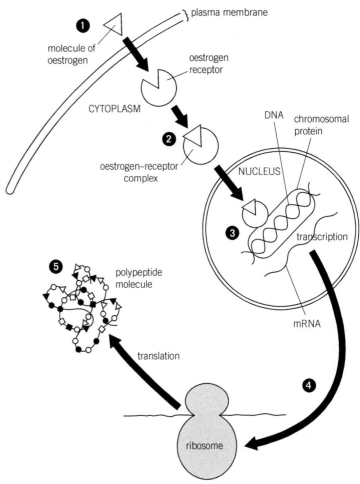

▲ **Figure 1** *The effect of oestrogen on gene transcription*

- siRNA combines with different proteins forming a complex called RISC (RNA-Induced Silencing Complex).
- The RISC complex scans the mRNA content of the cell in question.
- siRNA unwinds and one strand (called the guide strand) binds with its complementary length of mRNA.
- The binding of siRNA with its complementary length of mRNA causes the mRNA to break. Cleavage is catalysed by the enzyme argonaute, which is one of the RISC proteins.

As a result, translation is prevented and the gene is silenced.

Artificial siRNAs are tailor-made to be complementary to the mRNA of different genes. This means that siRNA can be used to silence specific genes. For example, silencing an oncogene would switch off the over-expression of the polypeptide stimulating mitosis. In theory the rate of mitosis would slow, perhaps stopping the development of a tumour. Our ability to selectively silence genes promises exciting developments in medicine and other areas of research.

Summary questions

1 What is a transcription factor? *(1 mark)*

2 Explain the effect of oestrogen on its target cell. *(3 marks)*

3 How does siRNA regulate gene expression? *(2 marks)*

20.4 Epigenetic control of gene expression

Specification reference: 3.8.2.2

Key terms

Markers: Groups of atoms that can bind to DNA and its associated histones, e.g. methyl (CH_3) and acetyl (CH_3CO) groups. Markers such as CH_3 bind to DNA, and directly modify its activity. Markers such as CH_3CO bind to histones, and indirectly modify DNA activity.

Epigenome: Formed from markers, directly or indirectly modifying the activity of DNA. Activity of the genome is modified by its epigenome.

Revision tip

When a cell divides, its genome and its associated epigenome are inherited by its daughter cells. The inheritance enables generations of cells to retain their specialised characteristics.

Revision tip

The temperature of the nose and tips of the feet, ears, and tail (body extremities) of many mammals is slightly less than core body temperature. The extremities of Siamese cats and Himalayan rabbits are darker than the rest of the body, because the genes encoding the production of dark pigment are only expressed at the slightly lower temperatures. The genes are suppressed at core body temperature.

Summary questions

1 Distinguish between the genome and epigenome.
   (2 marks)

2 Describe how the epigenome modifies expression of the genome.
   (5 marks)

3 The epigenome can be inherited by offspring from parents. Explain how.
   (2 marks)

What is epigenetics?

- We know that variations in the characteristics of organisms arise because of changes in the base sequence of genes (mutations) altering their expression and environmental factors affecting gene expression.

- Until recently, variations arising from environmental factors were thought not to be inherited because the base sequence of the genes of gametes (sex cells) was unchanged.

- Now, we understand that the base sequence of genes may remain unchanged but not only can environmental factors alter gene expression, and therefore the phenotype (characteristics) of an organism, but also the changed phenotype **can** be inherited.

Epigenetics refers to the study of inherited variations in phenotypes as the result of alterations in gene expression caused by environmental factors, and not just changes in the base sequence (mutations) of genes.

Methylation (see Topic 20.5, Gene expression and cancer) refers to the transfer of methyl groups to DNA, directly modifying its activity by:

- condensing the DNA – caused by histone combinations so that transcription factors cannot access the DNA

- stopping transcription factors from binding to DNA.

Overall, increasing methylation inhibits the transcription of genes, but its effects differ. If the methylated gene is:

- **a promoter**, then the process stimulated by the gene's expression is promoted

- **a suppressor**, then the process inhibited by the gene's expression is inhibited.

Acetylation refers to the transfer of acetyl groups to histones, indirectly modifying DNA activity by altering the degree of attraction between the negatively charged phosphate groups of DNA and positively charged histones:

- Increasing acetylation decreases the attraction, making DNA more accessible to transcription factors. Genes are switched on.

- Decreasing acetylation (deacetylation) increases attraction, making DNA less accessible to transcription factors. Genes are switched off.

Changing the epigenome and inheriting the changes

Lifestyle (the way we live), and other environmental factors such as differences in temperature, cause responses that may lead to changes in the epigenome. The changes alter gene expression and therefore an organism's characteristics.

When reproduction passes the genome from parents to offspring, most of the epigenome begins again in response to environmental factors. We say that the epigenome is reset. However, epigenomic markers on the DNA and associated histones of gametes may pass to offspring. In other words, the alterations in gene expression caused by epigenomic markers in response to environmental factors in parents are inherited by offspring.

20.5 Gene expression and cancer

Specification reference: 3.8.2.3

What is cancer?

Any environmental factor that causes a mutation is called a **mutagen**. Mutagens often cause mutations in the genes which control the rate of cell division. Normally cell division stops when the particular task requiring more cells is complete – a cut is healed, for example. However, if mutagens cause mutations in the genes controlling cell division, then the cells proliferate and cell division runs out of control. A mass of cells called a **tumour** develops.

If the cells of a tumour do not spread from the point of origin then the tumour is said to be **benign**. If they break away from the tumour and spread elsewhere in the body (**metastasis**), then the tumour is said to be **malignant**.

Carcinogens cause mutations in:

- **proto-oncogenes**, which encode proteins (transcription factors) that stimulate normal cell division. Mutated proto-oncogenes are called **oncogenes**. Their activity results in increased production of transcription factors stimulating cell division, or an increase in the activity of the transcription factors themselves As a result, cell division is over-stimulated and cells proliferate. A tumour develops.

- **tumour suppressor genes**, which encode proteins (transcription factors) that inhibit cell division, attach cells to one another and anchor them in their proper place, and repair damaged DNA before it can be replicated.

Mutation of tumour suppressor genes inactivates them. Cell division continues when it should stop and cells proliferate. A tumour develops.

Methylation

Addition of a methyl group ($-CH_3$) to a molecule is called methylation. Cytosine (C) bases of DNA accept methyl groups, and guanine (G) following cytosine is required for the enzyme catalysing methylation to work properly. CGCG sequences are, therefore, vulnerable to methylation.

Methylation usually inhibits transcription. The location of methylated CGCG sequences in places in genes that bind transcription factors inhibits transcription by:

- preventing transcription factors from binding to DNA

- attracting proteins that prevent DNA from unwinding from the histones that bind to it (the proteins cause deacetylation of the histones). Transcription factors are not able to access the DNA.

Many tumours are the result of hypermethylation (increased methylation). Because of hypermethylation of the promoter regions of tumour suppressor genes, the genes are inactivated and their transcription inhibited. As a result, expression of the genes' transcription factors is switched off (the genes are silenced). Because levels of transcription factors decrease, the rate of cell division increases. As a result, a tumour develops.

Oestrogen levels and breast cancer

The level of oestrogen in post-menopausal women tends to increase, because breast fat cells produce more oestrogen even though less is produced by the ovaries. The increase in oestrogen seems to increase the risk of menopausal women developing breast cancer.

If a cancer develops, then the level of oestrogen increases further. More oestrogen is produced by:

- the tumour itself

- white blood cells responding to the non-self antigens on the tumour cells.

This self-reinforcing sequence leads to the production of more and more cancer cells.

Key terms

Cancer: Malignant tumours.

Carcinogens: Mutagens which cause cancer.

Revision tip

Many of the chemicals in the tar of tobacco smoke are carcinogens that cause lung cancer.

Revision tip

Reduced methylation (hypomethylation) activates oncogenes which over-express transcription factors. Cell division is stimulated, cells proliferate, and a tumour develops.

Summary questions

1 What is the difference between benign and malignant tumours?
   [3 marks]

2 Explain why increased and reduced methylation each increase the risk of a person developing a cancer. *[5 marks]*

3 Why can the continuing growth of a breast cancer be described as an example of positive feedback? *[3 marks]*

20.6 Genome projects

Specification reference: 3.8.3

Genomes and proteomes

The term **genome** refers to all of the DNA in the cells of organisms. Studying genomes is called **genomics**. The aims of genomics include determining the sequence of bases of whole genomes (e.g. the human genome consists of 3.1 Gb) and identifying genes and locating them on their respective chromosomes.

Bioinformatics is the science of interpreting genome information using mathematical tools and supercomputers to discover: which genes express which proteins; interactions between genes (epistasis); and interactions between genes and environmental factors (epigenetics).

Benefits of the work include:

*   the potential of new drugs tailored to an individual's DNA (**pharmacogenomics**), reducing the risk of adverse drug reactions
*   the potential of treatments specific to the genome of different types of cancer
*   increasing the amount of food available as the result of novel crop and livestock breeding programmes
*   better understanding of fundamental principles of biology, e.g. evolution.

The term **proteome** refers to all of the proteins expressed by the genome:

*   Most enzymes are proteins.
*   Structural proteins (e.g. collagen) build bodies.
*   Transcription factors are proteins that regulate gene expression.

Proteomics refers to the study of protein structure and the role of proteins in the molecular biology of the cell.

Determining genomes

*   The **chain-termination** method can be used to determine the base sequence of the short strands of DNA of the genomes of simple organisms. The method was used to determine the base sequence of the DNA of the virus ΦX174: the first genome to be fully sequenced.
*   Determining the base sequence of the longer strands of DNA of the genomes of complex organisms, until recently, combined the chain-termination method with **shotgun sequencing**
    *   DNA is fragmented using specific restriction enzymes.
    *   Each fragment is sequenced to obtain a read.
    *   Fragmentation and sequencing is repeated several times to obtain overlapping reads.
*   Today the shotgun approach is combined with other sequencing technologies. These are more efficient than the chain-termination method, producing millions of reads in a day. Called **next-generation sequencing**, the tumbling cost of genome sequencing is the result of the fast throughput of data.

Determining proteomes

Bacteria are prokaryotic cells. Their cells are simple in structure and usually contain a single loop of DNA called a **plasmid**.

Bacterial DNA does not contain introns (non-coding lengths of DNA). Therefore determining the proteome of bacterial cells is relatively straight-forward. Eukaryotic cells (plants, animals, fungi, protists) are complex and contain DNA bound to proteins called **histones**. Eukaryotic DNA consists mostly of introns; only a small proportion (1.5–2.0% in humans) of the genome consists of exons (genes encoding proteins). Determining which gene(s) express(es) which protein(s) is difficult. Today, the **human proteome project** aims to identify all of the proteins produced by human cells.

Summary questions

1   Cells can produce many more proteins than there are genes encoding the proteins. How? *(2 marks)*

2   Explain the advantages of next-generation DNA sequencing over the chain-termination method. *(2 marks)*

3   What is an intron? *(2 marks)*

Chapter 20 Practice questions

1   The diagram shows the sequence of bases on part of one strand of a DNA
    molecule and two mutants of the sequence:

             A A T G G C G A T

    mutant 1   A A G G C G A T

    mutant 2   A A T G G T G A T

    a   What is the name of the type of gene mutation in mutant 1 and
        mutant 2?   *(2 marks)*

    b   Explain how each mutation will alter the part of the polypeptide for
        which this piece of DNA codes.   *(6 marks)*

2   Continuing research is making it more likely that treatments using stem
    cells to correct genetic disorders will become available sooner rather than
    later. Cystic fibrosis (CF) is a common genetic disorder. Mutation of the
    CFTR gene disrupts the movement of chloride (Cl⁻) ions out of the cells
    lining the airways. The normal gene encodes the polypeptide which forms
    Cl⁻ channels in the plasma membrane of the cells. People in whom the
    mutant gene is expressed produce too much mucus, clogging their airways.
    One possible form of treatment for CF using stem cells runs like this:

multipotent stem cells taken from CF individuals are genetically modified, replacing the faulty CFTR gene with a normal one → the genetically modified stem cells are stimulated to differentiate into airway epithelial cells → the differentiated genetically modified airway epithelial cells are transplanted back into the person they came from → the normal CFTR gene is expressed and the airway epithelial cells work properly

    Use the information provided and your own knowledge to answer the
    following questions.

    a   What is a mutation?   *(1 mark)*

    b   Explain why it might be better to use embryonic stem cells to treat CF
        rather than stem cells taken from the person with CF.   *(4 marks)*

    c   Give the advantages of genetically modifying stem cells taken from the
        person with CF and transplanting these modified stem cells into the
        person in question.   *(3 marks)*

    d   Explain why the Cl⁻ channel protein expressed by the mutant CFTR
        genes disrupt the movement of Cl⁻ out of airway cells.   *(4 marks)*

    e   Why is therapy using embryonic stem cells controversial?   *(2 marks)*

        Adult cells can be manipulated in vitro to produce embryonic-like stem
        cells. We say the adult cells are de-differentiated.

    f   Explain how the use of de-differentiated adult cells helps to overcome
        the controversy surrounding treating individuals with CF using
        embryonic stem cells.   *(2 marks)*

Restriction enzymes

The term 'restriction enzymes' will be used to refer to restriction endonucleases from now on. The enzymes catalyse the hydrolysis of the phosphodiester bonds linking the sugar–phosphate groups of each strand of a double-stranded molecule of DNA. Each one cuts at a point following or within a particular short sequence of base pairs. The short sequence is called the **recognition site**. The recognition site is **specific** to each restriction enzyme. For example, Figure 1 represents the recognition site for the restriction enzyme called *Eco*RI.

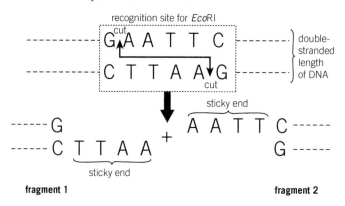

▲ **Figure 1** *Eco*RI: *its recognition site*

The recognition sequence is a palindrome, so called because the sequence GAATTC is the same as its reverse complement of bases CTTAAG. The fragments produced each have a short length of single-stranded DNA called a **sticky end**.

The exposed bases of sticky ends are 'sticky' because they form hydrogen bonds with the complementary bases of the sticky ends of the fragments of other DNA molecules cut by the *same* restriction enzyme.

Not all restriction enzymes produce fragments of DNA each with sticky ends. For example, the restriction enzyme *Hpa* I cuts at the same place within its recognition site, producing **blunt-ended (flush-ended)** fragments.

The lengths of DNA produced as a result of the activity of restriction enzymes form a mixture of fragments called **restriction fragment length polymorphisms**, RFLPs, or 'rif-lips' for short. The fragments can be separated according to size by **gel electrophoresis**. The fragment which contains the desirable gene may be identified using a **gene probe**. Once identified, cutting out the gene containing fragments from the **gel** makes them available for transfer into the DNA of another organism.

The genetic material of certain viruses is not DNA but RNA. The viruses (called retroviruses, e.g. HIV) produce the enzyme **reverse transcriptase** which catalyses the conversion:

$$\text{RNA} \xrightarrow{\text{reverse transcriptase}} \text{cDNA}$$

The single-stranded DNA produced is called **complementary DNA** (cDNA) because its base sequence is complementary to the base sequence of the mRNA from which it was made. cDNA does not carry sticky ends. A double-stranded molecule is produced by adding DNA polymerase to a mixture of single-stranded cDNA and DNA nucleotides. The enzyme catalyses the binding of the nucleotides with their complementary bases exposed along the single strand.

Summary questions

1 What is a recognition site? *(3 marks)*

2 What are sticky ends? *(3 marks)*

3 Describe how molecules of a single-stranded cDNA are produced. *(3 marks)*

21.2 *In vivo* gene cloning – the use of vectors

Specification reference: 3.8.4.1

Genes can be transferred from the cells of one type of organism to the cells of almost any other type. The cells of the organism into which genes are transferred are the host cells and are said to be **transformed**. The organism itself is **genetically modified (GM).**

A **vector** is a piece of DNA into which a desirable gene (a gene that produces a useful substance) can be inserted. The result is a mixed (hybrid) molecule consisting of vector DNA and the desirable gene. The term **recombinant DNA** refers to the hybrid molecule which itself is said to be genetically engineered.

Sticky ends

Inserting the desirable gene into a DNA vector is possible because of sticky ends. If the fragment of DNA containing the desirable gene is cut from the host DNA by a particular restriction enzyme which produces sticky ends, and the *same* restriction enzyme is used to cut the vector DNA, then the sticky ends of the gene-carrying fragment of DNA and the vector DNA are complementary and bond with one another. The nicks (gaps) left after bonding are sealed by the addition of phosphate groups. The reaction is catalysed by the enzyme **ligase**.

Inserting the desirable gene into a vector

Inserting the human insulin gene into the plasmid pBR322 illustrates how a gene can be inserted into a plasmid. Here is the process:

1   Restriction enzyme is used to cut DNA containing the insulin gene into fragments. Sticky ends are produced.

2   The *same* restriction enzyme is used to cut the plasmid vector. Sticky ends are produced complementary to the sticky ends of the DNA fragments.

3   The DNA fragments, some containing the insulin gene, are mixed with cut pBR322 plasmids and the enzyme ligase.

4   The sticky ends of the DNA fragments bond with the complementary sticky ends of the cut plasmid vector. After bonding, the nicks are sealed, catalysed by ligase.

The process 1–4 produces a mixture of plasmids, some unaltered, some carrying the insulin gene, others carrying other DNA fragments.

Inserting vectors into host cells

The mixture of plasmids and cells of the bacterium *Escherichia coli* are added to a hot liquid medium containing calcium chloride ($CaCl_2$):

*   Calcium ions (Ca^{2+}) increase the permeability of the bacterial plasma membrane to plasmids.

*   About 1% of the bacterial cells take up plasmids.

Marker genes

The pBR322 plasmid carries genes expressing resistance to the antibiotics ampicillin (Amp^R gene) and tetracycline (Tet^R gene). They are called **marker genes** because they can be used to identify host cells that carry a desirable gene (the insulin gene of our example).

*   Several restriction enzymes used to cut DNA containing the insulin gene into fragments have their recognition site in one of the resistance genes.

*   Insertion of the insulin gene inactivates the resistance gene in question.

The restriction enzyme *Bam*HI has its recognition site in the Tet^R gene. Insertion of the insulin gene inactivates the Tet^R gene. We will use this information as an example to continue the description of marker genes.

- A mixture of bacteria carrying the unaltered plasmids and the genetically engineered plasmids are plated on agar containing ampicillin.
- Bacteria without plasmids *do not* grow and form colonies.
- The bacteria that *do* grow and form colonies carry either unaltered plasmids or plasmids carrying the insulin gene inserted into the Tet^R gene. The colonies form a pattern on the agar plate.
- The pattern of colonies is stamped on sterile nylon cloth and transferred to an agar plate containing tetracycline. The procedure is called **replica plating**.
- Bacteria carrying unaltered plasmids grow and form colonies as the tetracycline resistance gene is intact, but those with plasmids carrying the insulin gene *do not* grow and form colonies.

Comparing the pattern of bacterial colonies growing on the tetracycline plates with those growing on the ampicillin plates identifies the colonies whose cells have plasmids carrying the insulin gene. The cells are present on the ampicillin plates but absent on the tetracycline plates. The colonies are cut from the ampicillin plates and cultured to confirm that they produce insulin.

Using genes conferring resistance to antibiotics as markers is an early example of ways to identify cells carrying particular genes. Nowadays **fluorescent markers** and **enzyme markers** are used. The methods are quicker and more efficient.

Summary questions	
1 Explain the meaning of the term 'recombinant DNA'.	*(2 marks)*
2 What are marker genes?	*(2 marks)*
3 Gene splicing refers to the insertion of a DNA fragment into a vector. Explain the role of ligase in the process.	*(3 marks)*

21.3 *In vitro* gene cloning – the polymerase chain reaction

Specification reference 3.8.4.1

Amplifying DNA

Forming multiple copies of DNA fragments is possible using the **polymerase chain reaction (PCR)**. The DNA is cloned.

Any fragment of DNA, including genes, may be cloned using PCR. Millions of copies of a DNA fragment can be synthesised in a few hours. The cloning process does not involve living cells. It is performed in labware. We refer to the technique as *in vitro* cloning. Figure 1 shows you the sequence.

Revision tip

When DNA is cloned we say it is amplified.

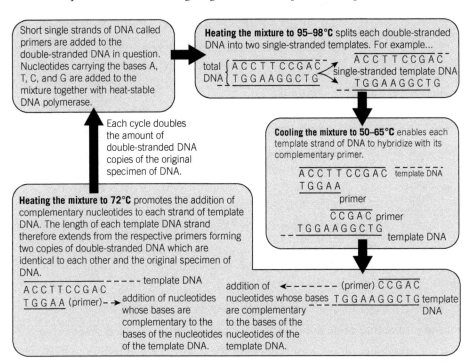

▲ **Figure 1** *The polymerase chain reaction (PCR). The cycle is repeated (25 cycles generate >1 million copies of the original double-stranded DNA). Each cycle lasts about 2 minutes*

PCR is widely used in biological and medical research. For example, it can be used to determine evolutionary relationships between organisms, and speed up the diagnosis of infectious diseases, genetic disorders, and different types of cancer.

Often only traces of DNA evidence are found at the scene of a crime. However, amplifying the DNA collected using PCR makes enough material available for analysis.

Relative advantages of *in vivo* and *in vitro* cloning

Testing drugs on animals and clinical trials which test the safety of new drugs on human volunteers are examples of *in vivo* techniques. Variables are more easily controlled *in vitro*.

Overall, *in vitro* techniques are often simpler, cheaper, and more sensitive than techniques *in vivo*. However, conditions *in vitro* do not correspond to real life conditions *in vivo*, and may produce misleading results. *In vitro* studies therefore, are usually followed up *in vivo*.

Revision tip

The size of DNA sequences:

Gb = giga base pairs (1 thousand million)

Mb = mega base pairs (1 million)

kb = kilo base pairs (1 thousand)

The human genome is 3.1 Gb.

Summary questions

1 What is the difference between the *in vivo* and *in vitro* cloning of genes? *(2 marks)*

2 List some of the uses of amplification of DNA by PCR. *(3 marks)*

21.4 Locating genes, genetic screening, and counselling

Specification reference 3.8.4.2

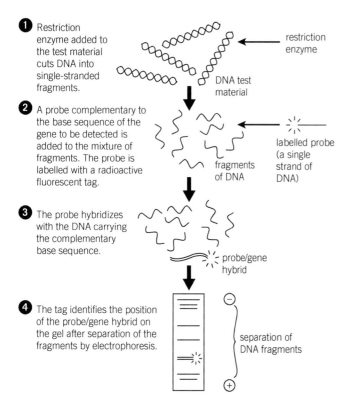

① Restriction enzyme added to the test material cuts DNA into single-stranded fragments.

② A probe complementary to the base sequence of the gene to be detected is added to the mixture of fragments. The probe is labelled with a radioactive fluorescent tag.

③ The probe hybridizes with the DNA carrying the complementary base sequence.

④ The tag identifies the position of the probe/gene hybrid on the gel after separation of the fragments by electrophoresis.

restriction enzyme

DNA test material

labelled probe (a single strand of DNA)

fragments of DNA

probe/gene hybrid

separation of DNA fragments

▲ **Figure 1** *Using DNA probes*

Revision tip
A DNA hybrid is a mixed molecule consisting of two DNA strands, each from a different source and each carrying bases complementary to its partner strand.

Revision tip
The work of genetic counsellors continues to expand as new developments in gene technology become available. Counsellors are not only members of a health care team, but are also employed by companies that develop and carry out genetic testing.

DNA probes

A DNA probe is a single strand of DNA. Its base sequence is complementary to the base sequence of the gene it is designed to identify. Figure 1 illustrates the technique of using a DNA probe. The test is carried out *in vitro*.

DNA probes and DNA hybridisation make it possible to identify and locate specific alleles of genes. The method can be used to identify the mutant alleles of genes responsible for different genetic disorders.

Genetic screening uses DNA sequencing, probes, and hybridisation to diagnose individuals who might have:

- mutant genes which cause genetic disorders
- variants of genes which in combination with lifestyle increase susceptibility to particular diseases.

Genetic counselling enables individuals to understand the potential benefits and limitations of screening before giving permission for testing. **Informed consent** refers to permission which is the result of advice from an expert; in the case of genetic counselling, a medical genetics expert.

Information obtained from screening is also used in the case of genetic counselling to discuss with individuals:

- the basic features of any genetic disorder or gene-linked disease
- the probability of developing the disorder or gene-linked disease
- the probability of children inheriting the disorder or gene-linked disease
- the options available to manage, prevent, or reduce the effects of the disorder or gene-linked disease.

For example, such information enables potential parents who are both carriers of a mutant allele of a gene to assess the likelihood of any children inheriting both recessive alleles and therefore developing a genetic disorder. In the case of oncogenes, knowing which ones are present helps in deciding the best course of treatment for cancers.

Summary questions

1 Explain how a DNA probe can identify a particular gene. *(3 marks)*

2 Explain why fluorescent tags are used in preference to radioactive tags to detect and locate genes. *(3 marks)*

3 What does 'informed consent' mean with reference to genetic counselling? *(2 marks)*

DNA: a unique fingerprint

A person's DNA is as unique as their fingerprints. Yet how can an individual's DNA be unique (except in the case of identical twins) when it is the expression of our genes that makes us all human beings? The answer is in the portion of our DNA that does not encode polypeptides/proteins.

Some non-coding DNA consists of base sequences that repeat themselves over and over again. The numbers of repeated sequences varies from individual to individual. The sequences are called **variable number tandem repeats (VNTRs)**:

- The lengths of VNTRs vary from person to person.
- Each one of us (except identical twins) has 50 to 100 types of VNTRs different from those of other people.

These differences are the basis of **genetic fingerprinting**. The procedure helps police to investigate crime. The DNA of hair follicles, blood, or other body tissues and fluids found at a crime scene is compared with DNA samples taken from suspects. The chances of the hypervariable regions of individuals (except identical twins) matching are millions-to-one. Therefore, matching genetic material from the crime scene with a suspect's DNA identifies that suspect as the likely culprit.

The different stages of genetic fingerprinting are:

Stage 1:

Extraction: double-stranded DNA is extracted from the cells of the body fluids and/or tissues found at the crime scene.

Stage 2:

Cutting (digestion): restriction enzymes are added to the DNA, cutting it into double-stranded fragments. Some of the fragments carry VNTRs.

Stage 3:

Separation: Figure 1 shows how the fragments of double-stranded DNA are separated on a gel by electrophoresis. Separation produces a pattern of bands which at this stage is invisible. The double-stranded DNA is broken into single strands by immersing the block of gel in an alkaline solution.

Stage 4:

Transfer: the single-stranded DNA fragments are transferred onto a nylon membrane. The technique is called **Southern blotting**.

Stage 5:

Hybridisation: after Southern blotting, the nylon membrane is immersed in a solution of DNA probes. Each probe is complementary to the core nucleotide sequence of one of the VNTRs carried on the DNA fragments. The probes are labelled with the enzyme **alkaline phosphatase**. In suitable conditions, the probes combine with their respective complementary DNA fragments carrying VNTRs. Each combination is an example of a DNA hybrid (a combination of DNA strands from different sources).

Stage 6:

Display: after hybridisation, the nylon membrane is covered with a phosphate-containing substrate and placed over an X-ray film in the dark. The phosphatase label catalyses removal of the phosphate from the substrate. The substrate fluoresces and the X-ray film 'fogs'. When developed, the film shows a pattern of bands. The pattern identifies the position of each DNA hybrid and is the genetic fingerprint (see Figure 1).

Stage 7:

Analysis: the 'bar code' pattern of the fingerprint obtained from the DNA found at the crime scene is compared with the 'bar codes' of suspects. If the 'bar code' of the one of the suspects matches the 'bar code' from the crime scene, then it is likely that the person is the culprit.

Uses of genetic fingerprinting

Apart from criminal investigation, genetic fingerprinting has a variety of uses in:

- determining genetic variability in populations
- finding out who is the parent of a particular child
- medical diagnostics
- guiding breeding programmes in zoos and agriculture to prevent inbreeding.

Revision tip

Fragments of DNA carry a negative charge. The mixture of fragments of DNA to be separated by electrophoresis is placed in wells at one end of the block of gel that sits between two electrodes. When the current is switched on, the separation of the DNA fragments begins. The negatively charged DNA fragments move to the positive anode of the electrophoresis apparatus.

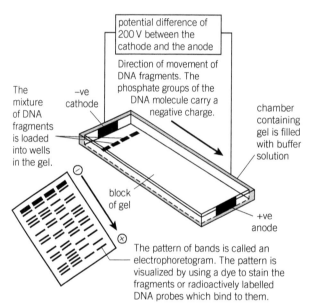

potential difference of 200 V between the cathode and the anode

Direction of movement of DNA fragments. The phosphate groups of the DNA molecule carry a negative charge.

The mixture of DNA fragments is loaded into wells in the gel.

−ve cathode

chamber containing gel is filled with buffer solution

block of gel

+ve anode

The pattern of bands is called an electrophoretogram. The pattern is visualized by using a dye to stain the fragments or radioactively labelled DNA probes which bind to them.

▲ **Figure 1** *How gel electrophoresis works*

Summary questions

1 What are variable number tandem repeats? *(3 marks)*

2 Summarise the different stages of genetic fingerprinting. *(6 marks)*

3 Do you think that evidence which depends on genetic fingerprinting is reliable enough to convict a suspect of a crime? Explain your answer. *(3 marks)*

Chapter 21 Practice questions

1 The polymerase chain reaction (PCR) makes it possible to synthesise large amounts of DNA from very small samples. The diagram illustrates the process.

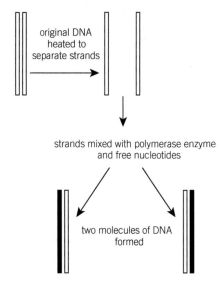

original DNA heated to separate strands

strands mixed with polymerase enzyme and free nucleotides

two molecules of DNA formed

   a Explain why the DNA produced in the reaction is identical to the original DNA. *(1 mark)*

   b At the end of the first cycle of the reaction, there will be 2 molecules of DNA. How many molecules of DNA will there be at the end of 5 cycles? *(1 mark)*

   c Why is the technique of PCR referred to as *in vitro* cloning? *(2 marks)*

2 A piece of DNA 10 kilobases (kb) in length was cut using the restriction enzymes *Eco*RI and *Bam*HI separately and together. The lengths of the fragments of DNA produced were as follows:

DNA	Sizes of fragments (kb)
uncut DNA	10.0
cut with *Eco*RI	8.0, 2.0
cut with *Bam*HI	5.0, 5.0
cut with *Eco*RI and *Bam*HI	5.0, 3.0, 2.0

   a The diagram shows the sequence of bases where the piece of DNA is cut by *Eco*RI:

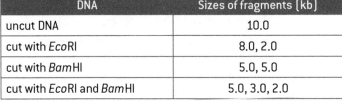

cut

---- G A A T T C ----
---- C T T A A G ----   } piece of DNA

cut

   i What is the sequence of bases called? *(1 mark)*

   ii The sequence is palindromic. Explain what this means. *(1 mark)*

   b How many fragments are produced when the piece of DNA is cut by *Eco*RI? *(1 mark)*

   c The fragments produced each have sticky ends.

   i What are sticky ends? *(3 marks)*

   ii Explain the significance of sticky ends. *(4 marks)*

Answers to practice questions

Chapter 11

1 Chromatography provided the means of separating the compounds extracted from the *Chlorella* culture; labelling with radioactive ^{14}C allowed the compounds to be located on the chromatograms. Photographic film darkens where the radioactively labelled compounds are located. [4]

2 The method stopped the light-independent reaction at known time intervals after the start of photosynthesis. It was then possible to identify the main compounds present in each sample at the known time. [5]

3 Absorbs heat from the lamp; maintains constant temperature. [2]

4 During the interval of 10 seconds between running off sample 1 and sample 2 for analysis, the amounts of hexose monophosphate and hexose bisphosphate have increased while the amount of GP has decreased. Triose phosphate and malate have appeared in sample 2. [3]

5 The changes suggest a sequence of reactions:

GP → hexose bisphosphate → triose phosphate or malate. [2]

Chapter 12

1 a Light intensity, temperature, and supplies of carbon dioxide and water are called limiting factors because if any one of them falls below its optimum then the rate of photosynthesis slows even if the others remain optimal; rate of plant growth maximised. [3]

 b Constant temperature; concentration of CO_2 maintained at 0.1%; constant illumination; sufficient water; limiting factors are optimal; the rate of photosynthesis is optimal; rate of plant growth is maximised. [4]

2 a w = glycerate 3-phosphate (GP)

 x = ribulose bisphosphate (RuBP)

 y = carbon dioxide (CO_2)

 z = ethanal [4]

3 a Proton gradient does not develop; protons do not flow through proton channel proteins (ATP synthase); ATP not formed by oxidative phosphorylation. [3]

 b Krebs cycle <u>and</u> link reaction stop; ATP formed <u>only</u> by substrate-level phosphorylation; during glycolysis; hydrogen (H) of reduced NAD / NADH; transferred to pyruvate; pyruvate reduced to lactate. [3]

Chapter 13

1 a 3% [2]

 b $\frac{1900}{3000} \times 100 = 63\%$ [2]

 c $1.2\,m^2$ [2]

2 a Total amount of energy received each year at ground level on the farm

 = 22 400 000 000 MJ [2]

 b Total amount of sunlight energy converted into plant tissue each year on the farm

 = 44 800 000 MJ. Apply formula given in question [4]

Chapter 14

1 a It increases the concentration of H^+ in the cell wall. [1]

 b It helps to loosen the bundling of the cellulose fibres of the cell wall. [1]

 c Both IAA and adrenaline bind to their respective cell surface receptors. Binding alters the shape of the respective receptor molecule. [2]

2 a Taxis: *directional* movement(s); in response to *light*; individual moves *towards* light (stimulus); positive phototaxis; moves *away* from light (stimulus); negative phototaxis. Kinesis: random *non-directional* movement(s); response to light (stimulus/light); moves faster; changes direction more frequently. [4]

 b Anhydrous calcium chloride absorbs moisture in air; creates concentration gradient of humidity / water in air; between parts (compartments) of choice chamber containing water and (anhydrous) calcium chloride. [3]

 c Woodlice in (choice) chamber move at random; woodlice enter dark *and* humid part of choice chamber; stop moving; after short time; most woodlice are resting in dark, humid part of choice chamber. [4]

Chapter 15

1 a The action of the sodium–potassium pump in the membrane of the axon stops. At 1.5 ms sodium channels in the membrane open. Sodium ions carry a positive charge (Na^+) and diffuse down their concentration gradient from the outer surface of the axon membrane to the inner surface, which therefore becomes more positive with respect to the outside. [4]

 b When the electrical potential of the inner surface of the axon membrane reaches +40 mV compared with the outer surface, its sodium channels close at 1.5 ms; potassium channels are open. Potassium ions diffuse down their concentration gradient from the inner surface of the membrane to its outer surface. Diffusion continues until equilibrium is reached. Activation of the sodium–potassium pump after 2.5 ms exchanges sodium ions and potassium ions across the axon membrane, restoring the resting potential. [Including time intervals demonstrates use of the graph in answering the question.] [5]

2 a Na⁺ channel prevented from opening by TTX; generation of action potentials prevented. [2]

b Repolarisation occurs; last longer because due only to closing of Na⁺ channels; not because K⁺ channels open (inactivated by TEA); TEA does not affect Na⁺ channels. [2]

c Hyperpolarisation depends on opening of K⁺ channels and efflux of K⁺; hyperpolarisation does not occur because K⁺ channels closed (inactivated by TEA). [2]

Chapter 16

1 a Detection of a change in temperature; brings about a response which corrects the change; body temperature therefore returns to its normal value. [3]

b The temperature-regulating centre of the hypothalamus combines inputs from skin sensory receptors; from within the hypothalamus itself; bringing about raised hairs/vasodilation/sweating (AVP appropriate responses); which control body temperature. [3]

2 a Insulin [1]

b Individual's immune system/B lymphocytes produce antibodies; that bind to (cell surface) receptors on beta cells of islets of Langerhans/pancreas; destroying them. [3]

3 The longer the loops of Henle, the more water passes from the liquid in the collecting ducts into the tissues of the medulla (of the kidney); the long loops of Henle of the kidney of a desert mouse enable the animal to conserve as much water as possible; helping it to survive in hot and dry environment; water conservation less important for survival of water vole (aquatic habit). [4]

Chapter 17

1 a 9:4:3 [1]

b Occurs when allele of particular gene; affects expression (activity) of allele of another gene. [2]

c Inheritance of alleles of two genes; independently of one another. [2]

d Recessive epistasis [1]

e Aa; Bb [2]

f Gene A (paired alleles): colour dominant; to albino; gene B (paired alleles) pink dominant; to purple. [3]

2 a

Group	(O−E)	(O−E)²	(O−E)²/E
Broken and banded	4.7	22.09	0.35
Broken and unbanded	(−)4.7	22.09	0.64
Unbroken and banded	(−)4.7	22.09	0.06(4)
Unbroken and unbanded	4.7	22.09	0.12

b 0.35 + 0.64 + 0.06(4) + 0.12; χ^2 = 1.17(4) [3]

c No correlation between banding in *Cepaea*; and predation by thrushes; *or* thrushes show no preference for either banded or unbanded snails;

because χ^2 is less than critical value at p = 0.05 / less than 3.84; (therefore) difference between observed and expected results is not significant / due to chance. [5]

Chapter 18

1 a 0.36, as stated in the question. [1]

b If the frequency of 'aa' is 36%, then q^2 = 0.36 and q = 0.6. Since q equals the frequency of 'a' then its frequency is 0.6. [2]

c Since q = 0.6 and $p + q$ = 1, p = 0.4. Since p equals the frequency of 'A', its frequency is 0.4. [2]

d Since p^2 equals the frequency of 'AA' and $2pq$ the frequency of 'Aa', the frequency of 'AA' is 0.16 (p^2 = 0.4 × 0.4 = 0.16) and Aa is 0.48 ($2pq$ = 2 × 0.4 × 0.6 = 0.48). [3]

e Because 'A' is completely dominant over 'a', the genotypes 'AA' or 'Aa' will express the dominant phenotype. The genotype 'aa' expresses the recessive phenotype. Therefore the frequency of the dominant phenotype is equal to the sum of the frequencies of 'AA' and 'Aa', and the frequency of the recessive phenotype is the frequency of 'aa'. Therefore the frequency of the recessive phenotype is 36% (see **a**) and the frequency of the dominant phenotype is 0.64 (16% + 48% – see **d**). [5]

Chapter 19

1 The limited amounts of available food and space limit population size. [1]

2 a The potential gene pool of the population of monkeys in each reserve is different. The smaller the population, the less genetic variation there will be in subsequent generations because of the restricted number of possible mates. This restriction in possible gene recombinations as a result of mating reduces genetic variation compared with larger populations. [4]

b *Any three of the following as part of a logical answer:* A large nature reserve is able to support a large number of monkeys. The greater the number of monkeys, the greater is the genetic variation in the population. The greater the number of monkeys, the greater the possible number of matings and therefore possible recombination of genes. The greater therefore is the genetic variation in the population from generation to generation. [You could include an understanding of the founder effect as part of your answer.] [3]

3 a Have the same genus name (*Sciurus*); different species names (*carolinensis*, *vulgaris*). [2]

b (Greys) more likely to survive; (therefore) (greys) more likely to reproduce; idea of differential survival; differential reproductive success. [3]

c Totality of all that a species population does in its habitat; all resources available to species population. [2]

d Compete; for same resources / food / hazelnuts. [2]

e i Only one species population; occupies particular niche at given time; idea of Gause hypothesis. [1]

ii Competitive exclusion of one species (from niche); one species becomes extinct; unless able to adapt to new niche. [1]

f Competition between individuals of the same species for resources. [2]

g i Control of population size. [1]

ii Individuals whose characteristics best enable them to obtain; resources in short supply; more likely to reproduce; favourable characteristics inherited; idea of natural selection; mechanism of evolution. [5]

Chapter 20

1 a Mutant 1 – deletion; mutant 2 – substitution. [2]

b A deletion alters the sequence of the bases downstream of the position where the mutation takes place. This alters the sequence of bases of the section of the mRNA transcribed downstream of the mutation, which in turn alters the sequence of amino acids translated downstream of the mutation.

A substitution also alters the sequence of bases but only within the codon affected and not downstream of it. This may change the amino acid unit encoded by the codon, or not, depending on whether the new codon is an alternative one for the same amino acid. The possibility arises because the genetic code is degenerate. [6]

2 a Change in base sequence of length of DNA / gene. [1]

b Embryonic stem cells (esc) are totipotent / pluripotent; differentiate into all/most types of cell; person with CF's own stem cells are multipotent (msc); differentiate into limited number of different types of cell; using esc greater flexibility / more options; differentiate particular type of cell / Cl⁻ channels (compared with msc). [4]

c Transplanted cells not rejected; because genetically identical with person's / patient's cells; (therefore) immunologically compatible. [3]

d Mutation alters tertiary structure of (Cl⁻ channel) protein; (because) amino acid sequence of protein altered; altering function of channel protein / not able to transport Cl⁻ (chloride ions); mutated structure not able to bind Cl⁻ (chloride ions); idea of mutated protein / Cl⁻ not able to bind / not compatible. [4]

e To obtain embryonic stem cells (esc) embryo destroyed; cultural / religious beliefs do not allow / not permissible to destroy embryos; accept ideas of sanctity of life / life begins at conception. [2]

f Embryos not source of (these cells); embryos *not* destroyed / used; (therefore) acceptable to (different) cultures / religious beliefs. [2]

Chapter 21

1 a The two new strands of DNA are each the complement of the respective original DNA strand against which they form. [1]

b 32 [1]

c 'Cloning' refers to the synthesis of multiple copies of DNA fragments identical to the original fragment. *In vitro* refers to the cloning process taking place in labware and not living cells. [2]

2 a i Recognition site [1]

ii The sequence GAATTC is the same as its reverse complement of bases. [1]

b 2 [1]

c i Sticky ends are 'sticky' because they form hydrogen bonds; with the complementary bases of the sticky ends of the fragments of other DNA molecules; cut by the same restriction enzymes. [3]

ii Sticky ends allow a desirable gene with sticky ends to be inserted into a cut DNA vector; with complementary sticky ends; the sticky ends of the desirable gene and DNA vector are complementary; because each is cut at the identical recognition site using the same restriction enzyme. [4]

Answers to summary questions

11.1

1 light harvesting: light energy captures by different pigments

light-dependent reaction: captured light energy enables photolysis and photophosphorylation

light-independent reaction: triose sugar produced by combination of carbon dioxide with hydrogen ions (H^+) derived from photolysis [4]

2 electron acceptor I: electrons released by pigment molecule of photosystem II (PSII); electron acceptor II: electrons released by pigment molecule of photosystem I (PSI) [2]

3 thylakoid membranes carry photosynthetic pigments; expose large surface area of pigments absorbing light; more light absorbed, greater rate of photosynthesis [4]

11.2

1 absorbs light [1]

2 photo-excited electrons ejected; from reaction centre chlorophyll molecules / primary pigments / p680 and p700 molecules [2]

Go further

a passage (transfer) of electrons (e^-) from one substance to another; substance losing electrons (e^-) is oxidised; substance gaining electrons is reduced

b energy released; enables transfer of protons; from stroma to intermembrane space; protons accumulate in intermembrane space

11.3

1 reduced NADP; transfers electrons / hydrogen; to glycerate (3-phosphate) / GP; producing glyceraldehyde (3-phosphate) / triose sugar / GALP [4]

2 reverse glycolysis follows sequence of reactions; glyceraldehyde (3-phosphate) / GALP $\rightarrow$ glycerate (3-phosphate) / GP $\rightarrow$ condensation reaction; fructose (bisphosphate) $\rightarrow$ fructose (phosphate); glucose (phosphate) / isomerisation $\rightarrow$ glucose [4]

12.1

1 a phosphate group; binds (to glucose molecule) [1]

2 makes glucose molecule; more reactive [2]

3 substrate-level phosphorylation; aerobic and anaerobic conditions [2]

12.2

1 dehydrogenation: removal of hydrogen atoms (proton / electron) from substrate; decarboxylation: removal of carbon dioxide molecule from substrate [2]

2 couples glycolysis with Krebs cycle; link reaction [2]

3 mitochondrion; matrix [2]

12.3

1 proton gradient does not develop; protons do not flow through the channel proteins combined with ATP synthase; ATP not formed by oxidative phosphorylation; Krebs cycle and link reaction stop; ATP formed only by substrate-level phosphorylation; lactate builds up [5]

2 electrons transferred along electron transport chain; oxygen final electron acceptor; energy released; energy available for active transport of protons (H^+) from matrix of mitochondrion; by way of inner mitochondrial membrane proteins; to intermembrane space; protons accumulated in intermembrane space; pass from intermembrane space; down proton concentration gradient; through proton channel proteins (embedded) in inner mitochondrial membrane; to which ATP synthase attached; passage of protons to matrix; releases energy; ATP synthesised; by combination of ADP with phosphate group [10]

12.4

1 hydrogen atoms (electrons) transferred to pyruvate; forming lactate [2]

2 decarboxylation of pyruvate to ethanol; releases carbon dioxide (CO_2); hydrogen atoms (electrons) transferred to ethanal; forming ethanol; muscle cells: hydrogen atoms (electrons) transferred from reduced NAD / NADH; to pyruvate; reduced to lactate (at least one correct answer to refer to each of yeast and muscle cells) [3]

3 amount (volume) of oxygen; required to metabolise excess lactate; accumulated during anaerobic respiration [3]

13.1

1 group of organisms; eating similar types of food (producers / consumers) [2]

2 primary consumers, herbivores, eat producers; secondary consumers, primary carnivores, eat herbivores; tertiary consumers, secondary carnivores, eat primary carnivores [4]

13.2

1 energy lost to environment at each trophic level; amount of food energy decreases as transfers from one trophic level to next; food energy available for transfer dwindles to zero [3]

2 animals do not produce enzymes/cellulase that catalyse the digestion; of cellulose; in plant cell walls; and lignin; in xylem [4]

3 warmer, greater rainfall; greater rate of photosynthesis; (therefore) greater productivity [3]

4 only one-step transfer of food energy; from producer to primary consumer; (therefore) less energy lost to environment; compared with two-step transfer of food energy; from producer to primary consumer to secondary consumer [3]

13.3

1 phosphorus cycle: weathering; release phosphates (ions) from rock; to environment (soil / water) absorbed by producers; transfer to consumers through food chains; decomposers release phosphates

nitrogen cycle: fixation; ammonification; nitrification; denitrification

comparison: rocks reservoir of phosphates (ions); atmosphere reservoir of nitrogen [6]

2 roots leguminous plants develop nodules; containing nitrogen-fixing bacteria (*Rhizobium*); release nitrates for other crop plants; released ammonium ions; nitrified by bacteria; forming nitrates [3]

13.4

1 natural fertilisers provide humus; artificial fertilisers do not; humus improves water / mineral content / aeration / drainage of soil [3]

2 nitrogen required for protein synthesis; magnesium (ions /Mg^{2+}) required for chlorophyll synthesis; reduced rate of photosynthesis / protein synthesis; reduced productivity; reduced crop yield [3]

3 ions; that enable enzyme catalysis to occur [2]

Go further

traditional farms grow crops and raise livestock; livestock faeces mixed with (bedding) straw natural fertiliser (manure); spread on land; provides nutrients for crops; if modern farm crops only (arable); manure not available; (therefore) artificial fertiliser needed

13.5

1 nutrient-rich water; growth of producers at surface more organic material; surface producers shade submerged producers; submerged producers die; organic material accumulates; increase population of aerobic bacteria / decomposers; increase BOD (idea of reducing dissolved oxygen concentration aerobic → anaerobic conditions); (therefore) fish / aquatic organisms die; further accumulation organic material; increase population of anaerobic bacteria; biodiversity reduced [8]

2 presence / absence of particular species indicates level of water pollution (idea that only species able to tolerate reduced concentration of dissolved oxygen survive, ALLOW: converse) [3]

3 nutrients (N, P, and K) are required for cell growth and cell division; mitosis; increased rate of cell division results in abnormal increase in numbers of algae [3]

14.1

1 stimulus: change in the environment (internal / external); causing organism to take action; response: action taken by organism; as result of stimulus [3]

2 positive tropism: *growth* response *towards*; unidirectional (most intense source of) stimulus; negative tropism: *growth* response *away*; from unidirectional stimulus [4]

3 taxes: *directional* movement; in response to stimulus; kineses: *non-directional* movement; in response to stimulus [4]

14.2

1 loosens bundling of cellulose fibres; lower pH of intercellular (between cells) environment; low (more negative) water potential of cells; water enters cells; by osmosis; increase hydrostatic pressure; causes cell elongation; enabled by more loosely bound cellulose fibre framework [6]

2 overall combination of stimulation / inhibition of growth; by plant growth regulators (factors); ensures plants maintain position / orientation in environment that maximises growth; because exposure to light (rate of photosynthesis); water and nutrients optimised (best possible) [4]

14.3

1 occurs without thinking / decision / conscious thought [1]

2 A receptor, detects stimulus; B sensory dendron, transmits (sends) nerve impulses to cell body; C cell body, axon extending from cell body transmits nerve impulses *away* from cell body; D synapse, gap between adjacent neurons; neurotransmitter released into synapse enables nerve impulses to pass from neurone to neurone; E relay neurone, links sensory neurone and motor neurone; F motor axon, transmits nerve impulses to effectors; G effector, muscle which contracts when stimulated by nerve impulses [7]

3 1 white matter; 2 grey matter; 3 neural canal [3]

14.4

1 convert one form of energy into different form of energy; ACCEPT relevant examples [2]

2 deforms (changes shape / stretches) capsule of Pacinian corpuscle *and* dendrite; membrane depolarised ACCEPT: description; produces generator potential; generator potential reaches threshold; triggers action potential [3]

3 sensitivity: intensity of light required to stimulate rods and cones; rods respond to less intense (dim) light; cones respond to more intense (bright) light; visual acuity: sharpness of detail seen; ref rods / cones: convergence reduces acuity [4]

14.5

1 sympathetic nerve opposes effect on vagus nerve, sympathetic nerve accelerates heart rate; vagus nerve inhibits heart rate [3]

2 baroreceptors detect changes in blood pressure; chemoreceptors detect changes in carbon dioxide (CO_2) concentration of blood; (therefore) changes in blood pH [3]

3 answer should include: increased heart rate; and consequences of increased heart rate, e.g. increased supply of oxygen (O_2) / nutrients to muscles; increased rate of muscle contraction [3]

15.1

1 [6]

Nervous system	Endocrine system
Nerve impulses are electrical; and transmitted by nerve cells called neurones	Hormones are chemicals produced by different endocrine glands; secreted into the bloodstream
Muscles or glands (called effectors); respond to nerve impulses	Hormones are transported in the bloodstream to all parts of the body; each hormone only affects its particular target tissue; because only that tissue has receptors which bind to the hormone in question
Effectors respond to nerve impulses in milliseconds	The response of a target tissue to its particular hormone is long-lasting

2 sensory neurone: long dendron, (proportionately) shorter axon; cell body not within spinal cord; motor neurone: short dendron, (proportionately) longer axon; cell body within spinal cord [2]

3 dendron carries nerve impulses *towards* cell body; axon carries nerve impulses *away* from cell body [2]

15.2

1 active transport; exchange of sodium (Na^+) ions out and potassium (K^+) ions in; across axon membrane; movement of ions against concentration gradient [3]

2 sodium (Na^+) ion channels; in axon membrane open; sodium (Na^+) ions diffuse from high concentration; outer surface of membrane; to inner surface; lower concentration [4]

3 protein channels components of axon membrane; only open when axon membrane depolarised [2]

15.3

1 answer should include: local circuits depolarise membrane; ahead of action potential; saltatory conduction (ALLOW jump from node to node) [2]

2 answer should include increase in axon diameter increases rate of transmission of nerve impulses; (therefore) more rapid / powerful muscle contractions; enable escape from predator [3]

3 action potentials form at nodes of Ranvier; jump from node to node [2]

15.4

1 potential difference (pd) across axon membrane; more negative (ACCEPT: value); than resting potential (ACCEPT: value) [3]

2 determines frequency of transmission of action potentials; direction of action potentials [2]

3 myelin sheath; large diameter axon; increase in temperature [3]

15.5

1 minute gap (visible only in TEM / 10 nm wide); between presynaptic membrane of axon (axonal know) and postsynaptic membrane of next neurone in sequence [3]

2 excitatory synapse: increase transmission of action potentials across synapse; inhibitory synapse: decrease transmission of action potentials across synapse; CREDIT: mechanism to include open and closed voltage-gated ion channels [3]

3 additive effect of EPSPs; generating action potential [2]

15.6

1 on arrival of action potential; cause movement of synaptic vesicles to move to presynaptic membrane [2]

2 catalyses breakdown of acetylcholine; prevents (interrupts) stimulation of postsynaptic membrane; prevents tetanus / permanent muscle contraction [3]

3 agonists: are stimulants; mimic neurotransmitter molecules; antagonists: are inhibitors; (because) bind to (postsynaptic) receptors [4]

15.7

1 threads running length of muscle fibre cell; consist of filaments; actin *and* myosin [3]

2
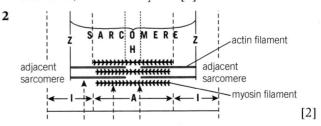
[2]

3 functional unit of myofibril between two adjacent Z-lines; consists of overlapping I-bands; A-band including H-zone and M-line [3]

15.8

1 actin and myosin filaments remained same length; whether sarcomere contracted or relaxed; pattern of light and dark bands (striations) changed during contraction / relax action of muscle fibre [4]

2 IDEA of actin filaments sliding over myosin filaments; (because) formation of actinomyosin crossbridges; myosin head tilts; pulls actin over myosin [3]

3 tropomyosin; blocks (covers) myosin binding site(s); on actin molecule(s) [3]

16.1

1 keeping conditions constant; internal and external of organism [2]

2 range of ways of achieving homeostasis; ACCEPT specific details e.g. polar bears; thick fur; layer of adipose tissue (fat poor conductor of heat); efficient blood circulation to extremities (paws) (supply oxygen / nutrients); small ears (reducing heat loss from reduced surface area) [4]

3 normal value (norm); stimuli; receptors; control centre; effectors; feedback; ACCEPT brief description of each characteristic [6]

16.2

1 reverses direction of change; from changed value *towards* normal value (norm); negative feedback [2]

2 reinforces change; *away* from normal value (norm) [2]

3 in hypothalamus; core body temperature rises; flushing/sweating/fever [2]

16.3

1 glycogenesis: synthesis of glycogen from glucose;

glycogenolysis: breakdown of glycogen to glucose;

gluconeogenesis: synthesis of glucose from non-carbohydrate substances, e.g. glycogen and amino acids [3]

2 endocytosis of hormone–receptor complex; complex stimulates Golgi apparatus; vesicles containing glucose carrier proteins bud off from Golgi apparatus; vesicle pass to cell surface (plasma) membrane; fuse becoming part of membrane [5]

3 cAMP is second messenger as formation of cAMP; follows activation of adenylate cyclase; by hormone first messenger; activates glycogen phosphorylase [4]

16.4

1 mutation [1]

2 individual's immune system destroys own tissues; mounts immune response [2]

3 genetically engineered human insulin same amino acid sequence; same structure as naturally produced human insulin; (therefore) injected genetically engineered human insulin does not stimulate an immune response [3]

16.5

1 glomerulus; Bowman's capsule; tubule; collecting duct; ureter; bladder; urethra [max. 5 for correct order, less 1 for each incorrect placing of word]

2 increases volume of forward flow / more blood; enters glomerulus; increases blood / hydrostatic pressure [3]

16.6

1 prevents passage of large molecules (proteins) and blood cells from glomerulus to lumen of Bowman's capsule [3]

2 regulate exchange of hydrogen ions (H^+); hydrogencarbonate ions (HCO_3^-); ammonium ions (NH_4^+), between capillary blood vessels (ACCEPT vasa recta) and lumen of tubule [3]

3 produce ATP; required as source of energy; enabling active transport; between blood capillaries (ACCEPT vasa recta) and lumen of tubules [4]

16.7

1 produce antidiuretic hormone (ADH); ADH is transported down neurosecretory axons; to posterior pituitary (gland); released into blood; passes to collecting ducts [5]

2 more ADH; walls more permeable; less ADH; walls less permeable to water [3]

3 aquaporins facilitate (make easy) absorption of water; from lumen of collecting ducts; to blood capillaries (ACCEPT vasa recta) [3]

17.1

1 **a** allele for long-winged = L, allele for short-winged = l [2]

  b long-winged fly =LL, short-winged fly = ll [2]

  c homozygous [1]

2 **a** Ll [1]

  b heterozygous [1]

  c Ll 2 : LL 1 [2]

3 **a** long-winged and short-winged [2]

  b test cross; the ratio of long-winged flies to short-winged flies is 1:1 [2]

  c a monohybrid cross [1]

17.2

1 **a** all F_1 plants; are purple [2]

  b 3:1 [1]

  c F_1 plants are heterozygous / each carry purple allele and white allele; purple (allele) dominant; purple parent homozygous / 2 purple alleles [3]

2 alleles occur in pairs; alleles at same locus (position) on homologous (pair of) chromosomes; alleles versions of the same gene; alleles may be homozygous (same)/heterozygous (different); dominant/recessive [3]

17.3

1 relationship between two values; showing how many times more one value is; compared with the other [3]

2 the larger the sample size, the less likely that randomness affects 3:1 outcome [3]

3 only two phenotypes; but 3 genotypes; homozygous dominant; heterozygous; homozygous recessive [3]

17.4

1 long wings = L, short wings = l, red eyes = R, white eyes = r [4]

2 ratio of phenotypes is 50:50; uppercase symbol: denotes the dominant allele; showing the dominant characteristic of the cross [2]

17.5

1 a genetic diagrams required for explanation if genotypes of parents are each I^AI^A; then the genotypes of children will be I^AI^A (group A); if the genotype of parents are each I^AI^O; then genotypes of children will be either I^AI^A (group A); I^AI^O (group A) or I^OI^O (group O) [5]

   b if genotypes of parents are each I^BI^B, then genotypes of children will be I^BI^B (group B); if genotypes of parents are each I^BI^O; then genotypes of children will be either I^BI^B (group B); I^BI^O (group B); or I^OI^O (group O) [5]

   c genotypes of parents are each I^AI^B; therefore genotypes of children will be I^AI^A (group A); I^BI^B (group B); or I^AI^B (group AB) [4]

   d genotype of one parent is I^AI^B; genotype of other is I^OI^O; therefore genotypes of children are either I^AI^O (group A); or I^BI^O (group B) [4]

17.6

1 autosomes: pairs of chromosomes (bivalents); each pair similar in size / shape in males and females; determine phenotype of individual other than sex (gender); sex chromosomes: different in size / shape; determine sex (gender) [4]

2 women can be carriers; normal / dominant allele on other X chromosomes; masks effect of X-linked partner carrying recessive mutant; woman homogametic; male heterogametic; normal / dominant gene *not* carried on Y chromosome; more men have the condition; women rarely have condition [6]

17.7

1 long-bristled and smooth-eyed; only phenotype appearing in F_1 [2]

2 12:1:1:3 [3]

3 long bristle, furrowed eyes / short bristle, smooth eyes; crossing over; during meiosis 1 (first meiotic division) [3]

17.8

1 answer should list and explain different types of epistasis; dominant; duplicate; dominant and recessive [4]

2 agouti (mottled coat colour) dominant; to solid coat colour (black / grey); recessive gene separate location / locus; encodes / previous pigment production; homozygous recessive gene preventing pigment production results in albino / no coat

pigment mice; even if pigment genes present; gene preventing pigment production epistatic to pigment-producing genes [7]

17.9

1 3; n = number of categories, 4; dof = $n - 1$ [3]

2 would be a significant difference; between observed (O) and expected (E) results; null hypothesis rejected [3]

18.1

1 total of all alleles; of all the genes; of a population [2]

2 absence of: selection; non random mating; gene flow; small population size; genetic drift; and mutations; ALLOW converse examples of conditions / influences disturbing allele frequency in gene pool [2]

3 0.25 (25%) (homozygous dominant); 0.50 (50%) (heterozygous); 0.25 (25%) (homozygous recessive) [3]

18.2

1 bases added; deleted; duplicated; inverted; substituted; and translocated [3]

2 continuous: all intermediate values; between extreme values of characteristic; discontinuous: no intermediate values / distinct categories [3]

3 dispersion (spread-outness) / variation of data; around mean value [3]

18.3

1 change in environment reduces or increases competitive intensity (ci); reduces (ci): reduces selection pressure; rate of evolution slow; reduced speciation / few new species / species change less likely; increases: converse of reduces [4]

2 natural selection is mechanism of evolution; how evolution occurs / takes place [2]

3 geometric increase over time; ACCEPT sequence 2–4–8–16–32–64–128, etc.; absence of competition / unlimited resources [2]

18.4

1 stabilising selection: selection against extremes of variation of characteristic; selection for average value / averageness of characteristic; little difference between characteristics of descendants of ancestors / little change in characteristics of genus / species; directional selection: selection in favour of (ALLOW for) one of the extreme values of characteristic; long term; genus / species change [4]

2 change in allele frequency; in population; over time / many generations; ACCEPT idea of change over time [3]

3 individuals with extremes of variation; of characteristic; selected for; individuals close to the average of the characteristic; selected against [2]

18.5

1 continental drift; mountain formation [2]

2 allopatric speciation is the result of geographical / environmental isolation; demes of original population diverge / evolve differently; different evolution results in sympatric speciation; inability of individuals of sympatric populations to interbreed / sexually reproduce; sympatric speciation result of allopatric speciation / not vice versa [4]

Go further

a does not stimulate the opposite sex to mate; even closely related species are reproductively isolated; different species maintained

b male of one species; unable to copulate with; female of another species

19.1

1 relationship between populations / species; between populations / species and the/their environment [2]

2 habitat: localised part of environment / ecosystem where (species) populations live; niche: totality of role of particular (species) population (what (species) population does); in its habitat [3]

3 refers to all characteristics of organism / species; favouring survival in particular environment [2]

19.2

1 answer to include description phases exponential; deceleration; stability [3]

2 the more individuals there are; in a population; the greater is the effect of limiting factors: ACCEPT examples, e.g. explanation of predator / prey interactions on respective population numbers, intraspecific competition [3]

3 crash occurs regardless of population size, limiting factors not responsible (for crash); caused by sudden change in abiotic environmental conditions / ACCEPT example, e.g. sudden drop in temperature [3]

19.3

1 physical factors in the environment; ACCEPT examples climate, altitude [2]

2 intraspecific: competition (for resources) between individuals of the same species / population; interspecific: competition between individuals of different species [2]

3 do not compete successfully for resources within niche; displaced from niche; do not adapt to the other niches (available) [3]

19.4

1 distribution of organisms; competition; predator / prey interactions [3]

2 effects regulating population growth; vary with; population density (numbers per unit habitat) [3]

3 fewer predators than prey; predators tend to reproduce more slowly than prey [2]

19.5

1 working: $(90 \times 80)/6$; 1200 [2]

2 avoids froghopper being noticed by predators; washes off / does not damage marked froghopper [2]

3 line transect fixed; method suitable for observing position of static (non-mobile) species (plants/limpets/barnacles); ACCEPT CONVERSE method not able to sample numbers; not suitable for mobile (moving) species [3]

19.6

1 primary: succession where organisms previously absent; ACCEPT explanation using particular examples, e.g. emergence of volcanic islands; secondary: succession where organisms previously present; ACCEPT explanation using particular examples, e.g. land clearance, deforestation [4]

2 flow of energy through communities of succession; increases; as succession; increases; as succession develops to climax; productivity increases (therefore); as succession develops to climax [3]

19.7

1 prevention of development of climax community; because of (through) human intervention / activities (long term) [2]

2 answer to include reasons: economic (including genetic resources); ecological; ethical; aesthetic [3]

3 sources of food; drugs; timber; dyes; oils [or another valid point] [3]

20.1

1 additions; deletions; duplications; inversions; substitutions [3]

2 U written instead of T for some of the codons [1]

3 sequence of base triplets downstream (after) point mutation; deletion or addition (DO NOT ACCEPT substitution); changed compared with sequence in non-mutated gene [3]

20.2

1 totipotent: potential to differentiate into all different cell types; pluripotent: potential to differentiate into most different cell types; multipotent: limited potential to differentiate into several cell types [3]

2 tissues damaged beyond self-repair; transplanting stem cells repairs damage [2]

3 embryonic stem cells: from totipotent; and pluripotent cells; adult stem cells: from multipotent cells [3]

20.3

1 proteins that regulate gene expression by initiating or inhibiting transcription [1]

2 oestrogen–receptor complex binds to specific chromosomal protein (ACCEPT histone); transcription of DNA bound to specific chromosome begins; translation into polypeptide [3]

3 silences / switches off / prevents transcription genes; CREDIT explanation of process [2]

20.4

1 genome: all the DNA / genetic material of an organism; epigenome: chemical modifications of the genome [2]

2 methylation: direct effect; condenses DNA-histone combinations prevents transcription factors; from binding to DNA; transcription inhibited; acetylation: indirect effect; alters charge on phosphate groups of DNA and histones / proteins; alters attraction between DNA and its histones / proteins; decreases attraction and genes switch on / expressed; increases attraction and genes switched off / not expressed [5]

3 epigenomic markers on DNA / histones of gametes / sex cells; may be inherited by offspring [2]

20.5

1 benign: cells of a tumour do not spread from place / point of origin; malignant: cells break away / metastasis from tumour; spread elsewhere in the body; CREDIT integrins and types of cancer cells tend to metastase to particular tissues [3]

2 hypermethylation: tumour suppressor genes inactivated; tumour develops; CREDIT detailed explanation; hypomethylation: activates oncogenes; over-express transcription factors; cells division stimulated; cells proliferate; tumour develops [5]

3 increase in oestrogen may increase risk of breast cancer in menopausal women; development of cancer increases level of oestrogen further; self-reinforcement results in increasing numbers of cancer cells [3]

20.6

1 polypeptide synthesis often result of combination of activity of two or more genes; number of combinations many more (exceeds) number of genes themselves [2]

2 reduces costs; faster through-put of data / result [2]

3 non-coding (for protein); length of DNA [2]

21.1

1 the point at which a restriction endonuclease / enzyme; catalyses reaction cutting DNA molecule; following or within particular short sequence of base pairs; CREDIT valid example naming restriction enzyme and base sequence of recognition site [3]

2 short single-stranded sequence of bases; form hydrogen bonds ('sticky') with complementary bases of sticky ends; fragments of other DNA molecules; cut by *same* restriction enzyme [3]

3 reverse transcription of mRNA; produces complementary strand of copy (c)DNA; catalysed by reverse transcriptase [3]

21.2

1 hybrid DNA molecule; consists of DNA from different species [2]

2 identify host cells; carrying desirable / useful / disease gene [2]

3 enzyme catalyses reaction that seals nicks; after piece of DNA inserted / spliced / pasted into another piece of DNA ; phosphate group added [3]

21.3

1 *in vivo*: genes replicated in living cells; *in vitro*: genes replicated in labware [2]

2 determine evolutionary / phylogenetic relationships; diagnosis of infectious diseases / genetic disorders / cancer; analysis of trace DNA evidence at a crime scene [3]

21.4

1 single strand of DNA; complementary to sequence of gene to be identified; labelled enabling location of gene to be identified [3]

2 avoids hazards of exposure to ionising radiation; reduces risk of developing cancer; risk assessment / health and safety [3]

3 permission given by individuals receiving genetic counselling; as result of expert advice from medical geneticist [2]

21.5

1 repeated short sequences of base pairs; called core nucleotide sequences; vary from individual / person to individual / person; found in non-coding DNA [3]

2 extraction; cutting; separation; transfer; hybridisation; display; analysis; ACCEPT items of process in correct sequence, DO NOT ACCEPT incorrect sequence [6]

3 reliability depends on correct procedures used when collecting DNA evidence from crime scene; if DNA collected is contaminated by DNA from source(s) other than individuals / victim / alleged perpetrator(s) of crime; compromises matching DNA fingerprint to suspect(s) [3]